Everything is

Always Changing

Cover Illustration and design: Evie Torrance
For all inquiries: evie@mindfullyevie.com

ISBN: 9798532144248

Everything is
Always Changing

by Mindfully Evie

Table of Contents:

Introduction

"Over the past two years, I've gone from bedbound, to housebound, to slowly venturing into the outside world. Writing down my innermost thoughts throughout each stage – holding nothing back – this book will take you on the journey with me, showcasing the challenges and joy along the way.

A continuation of growth and healing, I hope these words can remind you that life is neither light or dark but a tentative mixture of both. And I hope that by being open and vulnerable, you can find some strength, solace, and light amongst these pages."

About me

To understand my words, first, you need to understand my story. You see, I live with M.E, chronic Lyme and migraine. The experience of chronic illness is different for each person. For me, the main symptoms include incurable and overwhelming fatigue, fluctuating episodic to chronic migraine, IBS (irritable bowel syndrome), and MCS (multiple chemical sensitivity).

Introduction

My chronic illness journey started when I was sixteen and contracted glandular fever. It caused my health to spiral downhill, and now, eight years on, I still have not recovered.

My health journey took a nosedive at the end of 2016 when I became completely housebound a week before my twentieth birthday. I didn't end up leaving the house for nearly four years – becoming bedbound for the last one of those years. However, in April 2020 – just over a year ago – I started to see improvement for the first time. Since then, it's been ever so slowly uphill (with, predictably, a lot of standstills and setbacks along the way). So I'm now navigating a different stage of recovery that is hard but also filled with so much joy.

About the book

I published my first poetry and prose book about my experience of being housebound, titled 'Within These Four Walls,' precisely two years before this one. As soon as that book was released, I picked up my pen and carried on writing. So when I started writing this book, I was still bedbound. This continued for another five months until I began to improve. While 'Within These Four Walls' was a testament to my time being housebound, this book is a testament to my physical healing. But don't worry if you haven't read my first book – you don't need to have read it before this. You're simply joining me later on in my documented journey, and maybe this part of my story is more relevant to you anyway.

I knew the title of this book, 'Everything is Always Changing,' before I'd even started writing it. I'm not sure why. Those words just appeared in my head one day and stuck with me. I guess it was because I couldn't help but think, what's the point of writing another book when nothing has changed? And that's when I heard the words, but *everything is always changing*. So I knew that had to be the title for my next book.

The title was a reminder to me that even though my situation at the time was no different, that didn't mean I had nothing to say or no more lessons to learn. As I was changing, the things I was writing were changing too. Those four words were my vow to myself that I would write this book. It didn't matter that my situation hadn't changed – what mattered was that everything else was always changing.

You'll find in this book a collection of 'pieces' (as I like to call them): some longer, some shorter, half reading like poems, half continuous and broken prose, and all of them from my heart. The pieces in this book feel less like 'lessons learnt and wisdom earned,' and more like my emotions in that moment transferred onto paper. Trying to make sense of what I was feeling and how to get through it.

This book is split into three parts: Underground, Emerging, and Blooming. Unlike 'Within These Four Walls,' which offered different themes with each part, the pieces in this book are written and presented chronologically. Meaning the first part, 'Underground,' I wrote when I was still bedbound. The second part, 'Emerging,' includes the words I journaled for around the first six months of my improvement when things were still very delicate. Trying to understand if what was happening to me was even real. Finally, the third part, 'Blooming,' are the pieces I've written from the last few months when my improvement has been more solid. When 'in recovery' seems a phrase I can use now with more confidence. I also brought back the much-loved section, 'A Conversation with Wisdom,' but with a slight twist this time (I'll let you find out what that is)!

Due to the pieces being presented chronologically, there is a range of emotions within each part. Taking you through the highs and lows in only a few pages.

Even though I could have rearranged the words to help them flow more smoothly, it was important for me to present them as they came. The roller coaster, to me, reflects life and recovery more authentically.

While the mood of the pieces generally improves throughout, that isn't to say there's no happiness in the first part or any sadness in the last. In fact, recovery is so much harder than I thought. In many ways, recovering is harder than when I was surviving. Yet, in so many other ways, it's a million times easier. But instead of telling you about it here, I'll let my book tell the story instead.

Ending note

Whether you got this book yourself, were lent it by a friend, or picked it up on a whim, I want to say thank you. I'm so grateful for every single one of you joining me on this journey of continued healing and growth. I hope to offer back even half the strength that so many of you, my readers, have given me.

Love,

Evie xx

Part 1: Underground

Everything is Always Changing

THE BEGINNING

And here I am,
still waiting for the next
stage of healing to begin
so I can write a book
based upon these
new challenges,
showcasing
this changing journey
I am on.
But I'm still here,
still waiting.
No improvement,
no more energy,
no 'look how far I have come' words.
Just more heartbreak,
more frustration,
more hope gained and lost.
More treatments tried,
more 'I don't know what I can do,'
more 'I just want to get better.'
But through these struggles,
the stale-mate,
the un-moving,
comes more growth,
more learning,

Underground

more wisdom.
But with so little change
on the outside,
it is so easy to forget
the change
still happening within.
So here is my proof:
my dig a little deeper,
my plant the seeds even further,
to show myself,
to show you,
while nothing may be moving,
everything is always changing.

MEANING WHERE YOU ARE

And maybe while you wait
for the place you desire
on the other side
of the horizon,
you could fall into
where you are now and
discover something meaningful
that will make these days
all the more worthwhile.

❋

NEW MONTH

As I see a new month
coming my way,
I will be brave enough
to keep believing
that one of these months
will not end like the last one.
One of these months and
everything will be different.

YOU ARE NOT DEFINED BY YOUR PROGRESS

Whatever you have or haven't achieved, I hope you choose to rise above that. I hope you choose to remember that your self-worth is not tied to your productivity, progress, or things out of your control. I hope you choose to look back on your life with pride at all the times you chose hope over loss, peace over uncertainty, and to see all those small steps you took as huge leaps.

Don't beat yourself up for all the things you haven't attained or finished. You will have learnt other things along the way instead. You will have grown from the unexpected places and the struggles you faced. You will have expanded and stretched in more ways than you realise. You will have become someone else – someone fuller – without even knowing it. You have come *so* much further than you can possibly see right now.

It's also okay if you have made progress in some areas and not in others; there is so much time to do all those things you still want to achieve. You are allowed to see your progress as a mixture of both the ups and downs, steps back and steps forward, but always knowing you have grown through it all.

Everything is Always Changing

But above all else, I hope you know that even though
you might not have achieved all the things you want
to, you are not defined by your progress: you are worth
so much more than that.

❋

Look at you growing
so beautifully
and fiercely
each passing day,
breaking and
surrendering to
what the day brings,
knowing it
doesn't matter
if others can't see
your progress
as your footprint
was ingrained on this earth
long before they deemed
what was good enough
to be worthy.
Because you see it now,
don't you?
Your worth was
unconditional all long.

Underground

LIFE DEEP WITHIN

There is a life outside
these four walls.
I know there is,
because I was once a part of it.
Now I can only see it
through photos,
sounds drifting from
my bedroom window,
whispers of a world
out there.
But I also know
there is a life within
these four walls too.
My beating heart
reminds me of
the life so very
present in this room.
I feel it pulsing in
my fingertips,
the vastness of this
world inside me –
aching to be explored
and seen.

There is a life

Everything is Always Changing

in the discovery
of what lies within;
the dreaming,
the unknown,
the untraveled valleys,
the depths unseen.
There is a life
in the breaking,
the surrendering,
the rebuilding each day.
There is a life
in every breath,
each exhale and inhale,
reminding me of the
meaning and power
that quakes even here.

While I know there
will always be a life in
the world out there,
tantalisingly sweet
and alluring,
I also know
there is an unceasing
life deep within me.
And it will always be with me,
no matter where I am.

Underground

RUN TOWARDS THE LIGHT

And even though I have been caught
in the darkness more times
then I want to remember,
I'll never stop running
towards the unrelenting light.

I CAN DO HARD THINGS MANTRA

I have managed this before,
I can manage this again.

INTENTIONS

May this be the moment
you choose hope over loss,
pursue peace over uncertainty,
and practise letting go over resistance.

Everything is Always Changing

You are allowed to take a day away from everything. To forget the road you are on, the places you are trying to get to, the things consuming your mind with worry. To stop searching for answers, meanings, or solutions.

You are allowed to let it all go. To put it aside for a day, or even just a moment, as you get lost in a song, the stars, or a wave of peace or happiness so overwhelming that you forget about everything else.

It does not mean your progress will be halted or that you will fall behind. It means you are permitting yourself to see that this road you are on is long and hard. So it's essential to stop and get lost in these little moments that pass you by along the way. A day when you say:

'Today I will let go
of this road,
the unknown,
the search for answers.
I will give myself
permission to put
it all aside and spend
this day simply getting

Underground

lost with this moment
in front of me.'

※

Can't you see your effort
stained on your hands;
the layers of searching,
the knowledge you hold.
Look at how hard you're trying.
And I know you don't want to stop trying.
I know pausing the effort for a day
or even a week can feel like saying,
I'm fine with where I am.
But you must take time away.
You must remember to step back
from it all, letting the dust settle
as you take a moment to *forget.*
To forget the road you're on,
the places you've been, and just *be.*
You deserve that – no, you *need* that.
So go, find a book, a movie, a song,
anything that lets you get lost in
another world, just for a little while.

Everything is Always Changing

YOU MADE IT HERE

May you never forget
how far you have come.
May you never discredit
your progress or growth.
May you never compare your
journey with anyone else's.
May you never give up hope
that things will get better.
May you never stop dreaming and believing
that those dreams can and will come true.
May you never feel disheartened that
you are not as far along as you hoped.
May you never feel you are stuck;
like nothing is changing.
May you never stop practising gratitude,
letting go, and acceptance.
And may you never stop pursuing peace,
hope, and joy in the little things.
Because despite everything that happened,
you still made it through to another day,
and I'm so proud of you.

Underground

So many things may not have changed this past year. You may be in the same place physically; still trying to get towards the same goal you have been trying to achieve all year round, with little or no progress. You may even feel like you have gone backwards: stumbling into even more obstacles along the way.

But one thing is certain: just because the year gets closer to ending with each passing day does not mean your story is ending too. You are growing, and you are continuing along your path whether that day is the last day of the year or the first day of a new one. Your story does not stop or halt based upon where you are in the calendar.

It may feel disheartening because the end of a year, month, or even day, is often about reflection. Looking at where you have gone wrong and where you have gone right. The things you have achieved, and the things you haven't. But you are also welcome to embrace the fact that in terms of your story and where you are headed: there is no stop here. You are free to continue on ahead without looking back, and you are free to acknowledge there is so much more up ahead of you.

Everything is Always Changing

So even though it may be the end of another year or simply another day, I promise you, this is not the end of your story.

※

And with the stories of so
many trips around the sun
tucked into her back pocket,
she saw the never-ending
endless horizon in front of her,
knowing this moment was
merely a sentence in a book.
It might be the sentence
that made the story.
It might be the sentence
that was the beginning
or end of a chapter.
But right now,
that didn't matter.
Because with the courage
of the mountains and valleys
she'd already shattered through,
she still knew
one unbreakable truth:
this was not the end of her story.

Underground

HONEST TRUTH

I am more than my illness,
but sometimes,
my illness feels more than me.

✷

CRASH

It doesn't matter how many
times it has happened before,
it still hurts when you lose
the progress you thought
you had made.

✷

KEEP GOING

You can do everything right
and things can still go wrong.

The key is to never
stop doing right.

Everything is Always Changing

DESPERATE FOR AN ADVENTURE

I like to search places
I hear of in passing,
dropping the little yellow figure
on google maps onto the ground
and go for a walk around the streets.

I've never told anyone I do this.
I don't know if anyone else does it too.
It's a strange experience,
exploring the world
through a screen.
And yet I'm still speechless
at the views I stumble across,
holding my breath at the wonder
I didn't know existed.
It's like I forget how big the world is
outside of my bedroom.

I wish I could walk
into the houses
and talk to the people.
I wish I could see their lives,
find out the places they've been to,
listen to the stories needed to be told.
But the yellow figure doesn't let me.

Underground

So instead I have to suffice
with seeing their homes from
the outside, absent of life.

Once the ache for adventure
becomes too much
for my heart to contain,
I turn off my screen,
mentally adding another name
to the endless list
of places I want to visit.

When I lie back down
and close my eyes,
I'll walk the streets again
in my mind,
over and over,
adding in the smells,
sounds, and stories
I couldn't get
from the little yellow figure
on the screen.
And then, once the ache has passed
and the desperation kicks in,
I'll hear of another place in passing,
turn back on the screen,
and start my adventure again.

Everything is Always Changing

LOCATION

Maybe life is not about
our physical location,
but our location
within ourselves.
Do we live on the surface,
afraid to go any further?
Or do we take the leap,
living life deep within our soul.
Do we know who we are:
who we really are,
away from the noise
and the outside world?

Maybe we should focus less
on where we are in the world,
and spend more time going underneath:
bringing light to the cracks and corners,
exploring the deserted vessels,
breaking our bones and looking inside,
knowing somewhere down here
we might find our location.
Somewhere deep within,
we'll find our infinite source of life.

Underground

RARITY

Looking out the window,
I see a sunset stretching across
the vast horizon,
alighting the skies with its fire.
It is a view so
breathtakingly beautiful,
for a moment,
I'm left speechless.
Just for a second,
my thoughts tumble
out of my head
and my voice rolls
out of my mouth.

It's these moments you
want to capture,
you want to describe,
but nothing can ever do
how you feel justice.
All you know is you think:
I want more of this.
I don't know what it is,
but whatever it is,
I want it.
If it was sold,

Everything is Always Changing

I'd buy it in gallons.

It feels something
like stillness,
like swallowing sunlight;
an array of colours
so vivid and warm,
it melts you completely.
Just for a second,
you forget who or where you are.
All you can think of is
the beauty in front of you.
It is freedom and bliss
wrapped up in one.

But then the wind comes,
and you lose the moment
in the breeze.
You feel its absence
as it leaves your body.
But you're also still
so lost in the moment,
so grateful that you got
the chance to feel it at all.

And so you wait
for the next moment

Underground

like that one to arrive.
But it is never a moment
you can plan – no.
It is a moment that always
captures you unaware,
for that is the beauty of it.
And although it doesn't
last long enough for you to grasp
the feeling it gave you,
the memory of it lingers around,
like salt left on your lips
after a swim in the ocean.

You don't need to look
for reasons to be happy:
the reasons are already here
in front of you.

(open your eyes,
there is so much
astonishing beauty
already on
your doorstep)

Everything is Always Changing

There is this idea that we should chase life: seize the moment, take chances. But what I think we often forget is that while there is always a life in front of us to chase, there is also always a life behind us. It follows wherever we go: through the ups and downs, the stillness and quiet. Its presence is so unobtrusive that we can forget it is even there.

So we might say we're missing out on life, thinking the only life there is is the one ahead of us. But we're forgetting to acknowledge the life that is with us right now. It breathes into our every moment, pulsating through our body, never leaving our side.

So if you feel like life is happening without you, remember that life has never left your side. You are not missing out on anything: life is following you through everything. It will always be here with you, and it will never leave.

Underground

Another year come and gone.
No further from being free from this
than I was three years ago.
Dreams of blue skies,
open roads,
and life outside this house
slip further away still.
I don't know what I'm doing wrong.
I don't know what I'm doing right.
In the darkest hours,
the questions of
'Is this all in your head?'
slip up from old surfaces
that people, doctors,
and history have left behind,
making me feel that maybe
these three years are self-inflicted
and this confinement
is somehow my choice.
These thoughts are ever so fleeting
but oh so devastating.
This is what being ill with an illness
so misunderstood can do to you:
it can take the physical facts of your reality
and twist them again and again

Everything is Always Changing

until even you start to question
if it's all in your head.
But it's not. I know it's not.
It could not be more real or evident;
I feel the weight of the fatigue in my bones,
in every breath I take,
pulling me downwards
like it has a gravitational hold on me.
And so I submerge the thought
that I have subconsciously
inflicted this pain
upon myself,
drowning out the idea that this is my fault,
and pull out the evidence that:
this is not my fault,
I didn't cause it,
there is nothing I am doing that
is causing me to stay in this place.

END DATE

One of the hardest things about being chronically ill is not knowing the end date to it all; the 'chronic' part of chronic illness. It's not knowing when you'll get better, how long it will take, or what the future looks like.

It's not like those times in life when you have to endure something gruelling but you have an end date in sight. It's easy in those situations to say, 'Only X more days left, you can do this.' 'Not long now, keep going.' But when you live with a chronic illness, you don't get to have those reassuring mantras. You have no idea how long you have to keep going or how many days are left.

Most of us chronically ill have already endured so much. Endless days of hard work, courage and perseverance. It becomes so easy to forget that there will one day be an end date to all of this. There will be a day when you wake up and your first thoughts won't be what supplements you have to take or how you have to pace yourself – rearranging and cancelling activities, adding in rest periods to cope.

There will be a time when you wake up and your first thoughts will be of the endless opportunities the day brings. To realise that all illness-related thoughts no longer take centre stage in your mind. Instead, thoughts of life, hope, energy, and possibility will become second nature to you.

So even though I have no end date yet, even though I have no idea how much longer I'll have to endure all of this, that doesn't take away the fact that the end date is there. It is still very real, still very achievable, and one day I will reach it, and so will you too.

❄

> Even though I don't know how
> or when I'll get there,
> I still know I will make it.

....

(I want to add that I know not everyone with chronic illness has the luxury to recover. I know some chronic illnesses are life-long, and rest is a privilege. And I know I *am* privileged. I'm one of the lucky ones not to have any responsibilities other than to look after myself. I'm so lucky to have a family who can look after me, a quiet house to rest in, and financial support. So I want to acknowledge everyone who doesn't have these advantages. I want to add these words for you.)

WARRIOR

I am not a warrior
because I'm fighting to get better.
I am a warrior
because I choose to surrender
to the life I have here,
whilst trying to build
the foundation
for a more stable future.
People think warrior
means you are fighting;
resisting the life you are living.
But it's easy to fight the thing
you don't want in your life.
What's not easy
is showing up
again and again
to the pain;
embracing it
with love and kindness.
What's not easy
is finding meaning
in a life deemed
meaningless by society.
What's not easy
is getting by in a world

Everything is Always Changing

not adapted for you
or providing an environment
for you to succeed in.
What's not easy
is finding moments of
peace,
acceptance,
and surrender,
amongst
the grief,
loneliness,
and pain.

Warrior is not about
fighting with the name
of what you've been
made to live with,
but about surrendering
to the moment
and finding a life
alongside it.

Underground

STILL HERE

The fact you're still
showing up every day
is a sign that you're doing
better than you think.

✻

IT IS STILL BRAVE

Just because you have
no choice to live this way
doesn't mean it still isn't brave.

✻

A REMINDER FOR YOU

In case no one has told you recently:

I am so proud of you for every moment
you have got through to reach this one.
And I am so proud of you for every
future moment you will get through too.

WILDFIRE

Life will test you. It will test you over and over again until your bones ache and your chest collapses in on itself, crushing your heart beneath. You will have so many moments where you think: *I can't go on, I can't do this anymore*. It's almost cruel how much life will repeatedly ask more from you: more courage, more rebuilding, more overcoming.

But know this: each time, you will rise. It may take a day, week, or month, but you will find your strength again from an unearthed place within. You will carve out a way back to the light and move forward with a boldness and fire that you didn't know you had.

So remember, my darling, this life may shatter you into a thousand pieces; leaving scars on your palms and splinters in your heart. And yet, each time, it will only ignite the endless wildfire within you. You will stand, again and again – as many times as you have to – burning so brightly others will see your light all the way from across the horizon.

So keep going. Keep finding the courage to rebuild yourself over as many times as you need to. Keep rising when this life breaks you down. And know, deep within you, there is an unrelenting wildfire that will never burn out.

SOFTER

Some things
may never stop hurting.
But over time,
those wounds
become softer;
you can carry
them a little easier,
like a scream
turning into a whisper.
You start to accept
what's been has gone,
but you are allowed
to look ahead
and move forward,
knowing there is more
to you and your story
on the horizon.

SOFT PLACES WITHIN

We often talk about this idea of going to places where we feel free, where we can breathe and feel ourselves. But what if those places are also inside of us? What if the places we need to go to are the soft and safe spaces within:

The quiet, gentle pockets that let us sit without question, holding us with unrelenting love and tenderness.

The gaps that let us breathe and give us room to be, making space for our emotions to run their course.

The silent voice that doesn't ask us what this means or where we're going or what will happen, but just lets us sit quietly, free from thought.

The place that tells us with certainty that we're going to be okay. And not needing to make sense of why or how we'll be okay, but just a raw, tender knowledge that we will.

So maybe next time you feel the need to run somewhere where you feel you – to find a freedom and place where you can breathe a little easier – maybe run inside yourself first. Bury yourself amongst the passages and corridors until you find the door that you're looking for; the room that asks nothing from you and takes nothing away. But just sits quietly in the depths of your soul, waiting for you to remember to come down and visit this soft space within again.

How beautiful it is
that there is a place
inside of you
so soothing and warm,
like honey and sunlight,
whispering soft words
of reassurance and comfort.
How sweet it is
to know you can
visit this place
when *out there*
becomes too much.
That you can dive deep
beneath the salty waves
into this endless ocean,
letting this soft space
hold you for a while
until you feel *you* again.

Underground

In case no one has told you recently,
just getting through each day is an
amazing achievement.

※

When everything feels heavy,
remember, it's okay to...

Put yourself first.
Turn off the news.
Prioritise self-care.
Avoid negativity.
Not reply to messages.
Feel a bit shit.

※

Don't let other people tell you
how you should be feeling –
your emotions are always valid.

Everything is Always Changing

WHAT NOT TO SAY TO SOMEONE WHO'S STRUGGLING...

It could be worse!
it could also be a lot better

At least it's not cancer.
my experiences are still valid

You just need to try
yoga/meditation.
*I don't need you
to fix me*

Just think positively!
*this is unrealistic and
unhealthy*

You are in charge
of your emotions.
*then no one
would be sad*

I don't know how you
get through it all.
I don't have a choice

Just focus on the
good things in life.
*I can't heal from
my pain if I ignore it*

I know someone who
had that, they just did...
*please don't give
unsolicited advice*

Everything happens
for a reason.
this isn't a universal belief

Underground

And out of nowhere,
the weight of
the unspoken trauma,
the memories,
the flashbacks,
come flooding back.
These moments
are stained on the inside of my mind,
and no matter how much
I try and bury them,
keeping them away
from seeing the light of day,
they are still there,
wanting to burst through.
But I also know these memories
are allowed to stay buried.
I don't need to go back there.
I don't need to open old boxes
that hold nothing good for me.
I know in my heart
I can stand on top
of these moments:
letting them fall
beneath me.
Knowing,

Everything is Always Changing

right now,
I am free
to leave
the shadows behind,
coming back to
this moment,
searching for an
inhale of peace
as I whisper to myself...

Stay present.
Stay present.
Stay present.

❄

There is a reason
your shadow always
falls behind you;
it's showing you the
darkness is in looking back
– in turning around.
But you don't need
to glance that way,
you can look forwards:
the light is ahead of you.

Underground

Here is your reminder that you don't have to be happy all the time. It doesn't matter if it's the weekend, you're on holiday, or it's Christmas. You're still only human.

So don't put pressure on yourself to push through, force a smile, put on a facade. Make sure you still allow room for sadness, grief, loneliness, and mourning. Remember, if you make space for the sadder emotions, there will still be plenty of room left for the happier emotions too: you can always feel both at the same time.

✻

Who taught you that life
could only be light or dark?
Who told you that you couldn't
be happy and sad, accept and grieve?
Because you can feel both:
life is not an either-or recipe.
It's a mixture of sweet and salt;
of honey and lemon.
And this is okay:
it's okay to feel both.
There is no *right* way to feel.

THE BEST PLACE TO BE

I hope amidst the chaos of goals, intentions, and reflections, you take moments to breathe. To breathe in the calm and breathe out the unknown. To remember this moment is the only moment that matters: that the future does not exist and the past is merely a memory.

I hope you treat this moment like it was meant to be lived: fully engaged, fully alive, with nothing but thoughts of what is right in front of your eyes. I hope this deep breath reminds you that everything is going to be okay. I hope it reminds you to take things one moment at a time. That life unfolds only as you live it, not as you planned.

Because to be here in the moment, to live life as it is happening, is the most important thing you can do for yourself, your happiness, and your peace. This moment, this breath, is the best place in the world to be.

Underground

FEELING THAT THING YOU DON'T WANT TO FEEL

I rarely feel sad. I know many people don't believe me when I say that, given my situation, but it's true. Yet, when sadness does come creeping up on me, I often forget it's okay to feel it.

The other day, I was emotionally triggered by something unasked for and out of my control. I instantly felt myself fall into a whirlwind of emotions. But because an outside force caused these feelings, I was determined not to let them ruin my day. So I tried to push the emotions away, thinking I could somehow outrun them.

But then I remembered something I'd written a little while ago: *You need to feel that thing you don't want to feel.* Seeing these words made me realise I had to let the sadness come. I had to embrace it completely. And so I did. I finally felt the sadness and frustration that had been building for a while.

Once I'd embraced the heaviness, the sadness lost its weight. And it wasn't long before I could let it go too. But it doesn't matter how many times I know this cycle – embrace, feel, release – I still need my own reminder. I can still forget I should be embracing when I'm caught up in resisting. So remember: one of the bravest things you can do is to feel that thing you don't want to feel.

❋

Look at you,
so bravely
stopping
to let the pain
you had been
running from
roll over you,
like the rain
finally catching up
with the thunder.

Take heart,
the skies
will clear
again soon.

Underground

I AM NOT INVISIBLE

You say I'm invisible
but can't you see
how much my life has changed:
no more school,
no more work,
no more socialising.

You say I'm invisible
but can't you see
how it affects my family:
full-time carer,
cancelled holidays,
the worry in their eyes.

You say I'm invisible
but can't you see
the pain I'm in,
the leaving early,
the cancelled last-minute,
the you haven't heard from me
'cas I did a thing yesterday.'

You say I'm invisible;
that you can't see me.

Everything is Always Changing

Come,
look closer.
You'll see me.
You'll see the pain.
You'll see the life changed.
You'll see the effort to look normal.
You'll see the loneliness, grief,
sadness and frustration.
You'll see the ripple effect my illness
has had on my life and those I love.

You'll also see a fighter.
You'll see someone trying so hard to get better.
You'll see the daily acceptance, surrendering, and
letting go.
You'll see the extra love I'm pouring into my body
and soul, reminding myself it's going to be okay.
You'll see the unrelenting resilience, courage and
bravery it takes for me to get through each day.

Come and look around me too:
you'll see all the other
warriors,
healers,
and just-trying-to-get-by-ers,
like me out there.

Underground

Why can't you see me.
Why can't you see me.
Why can't you see me.

Do you see me now?

HARD TO LOVE

I used to think people would have to love me in spite of my illness. I used to see my illness as something some people might not be able to 'handle.' I assumed it was the baggage I carried around with me. I even believed my illness could be the cause of someone else's unhappiness. Because of this, I often let others mistreat me.

It also didn't help that some people who stuck by me when I first fell ill made me feel hard to love. They made me feel like they were doing *me* this huge favour by staying. So I let them do and say things that most people wouldn't as repayment for sticking around. I thought this was okay. I thought it was only fair. Truthfully, I was just so relieved that someone had stayed despite my baggage that they could treat me any way they wanted and I wasn't going to say anything.

It took me years to realise the people I now allow and keep in my life don't love me despite my illness; they love me as a result of my illness. They love the person I've become. They love how my illness has not only changed my perspective but theirs too. They love how my illness has brought us closer. They love supporting me through the good and bad times. To put it simply, they love me as a whole; all illness and non-illness parts included.

To feel like your illness is a burden to others is an easy trap to fall into. Even now, I can find myself getting caught. But your illness should never make you feel unlovable or unworthy of love. It should never feel like a burden you bring to a relationship or friendship. Yes, inevitably, it may bring some difficulties. But if your situations were reversed, wouldn't you want to stay by their side? If you don't have a problem with your illness, then neither should they.

Don't ever allow anyone to use your illness against you. Don't ever let anyone make you believe that you are unlovable. Find people in your life who will make you question why you ever thought that in the first place.

Everything is Always Changing

THOUGHTS ON RELATIONSHIPS AND ILLNESS

You deserve love even when you're sick.

Some of the best and most supportive
people you will find are online.

Don't let other people make you feel guilty
for cancelling last minute.

It's better to be on your own than to be friends with
people who don't hold your best interest at heart.

Clearly communicate your needs
and boundaries to others.

Realise that they don't have to understand
completely in order to love and support you.

Someone's love for you shouldn't be
dependent on your recovery.

Accept that not all relationships last.

Be grateful for this opportunity to learn
who your true friends are.

Underground

I'LL HOLD THE LIGHT FOR YOU

As I looked into her face,
I could see the pain
of my younger self
mirrored in her eyes.
So many things
I wanted to say to her –
it will be okay,
you won't always feel this way,
you're allowed to feel sad,
healing takes time.
But I knew nothing
would pass her exterior
as nothing penetrated mine
when I was younger and in pain
except my own words and beliefs.
So instead I held her pain
in my arms, telling her:
I know you can't see
the light right now,
so I will keep shining for you,
and hold it until you are ready
to embrace it for yourself
once again.

Everything is Always Changing

For those seeking out a word to heal them, an instruction manual to make them feel better overnight: know that by doing this, you are getting in the way of your own healing. You are making yourself believe these whispers of hurt just need a quick fix. But these wounds inside of you go so much deeper than that.

Healing is a journey, a daily practice. It takes so much work to heal, to undo the hurt. But please know, it is also *so* worth it. It is worth the effort it will take.

So take your time to go within; to seek out the truths and unravel things one breath at a time. Remember, healing is a lifelong journey. But you can do it. You can walk along this tender path of growth and change.

✳

When you break a bone, you don't
rush straight into exercises to heal it.
Instead, you sit and wait for the bone
to heal. Do the same with yourself –
do not rush to 'fix' what's wrong when
things hurt. It's okay to stay with the
brokenness for a while and let it breathe.

Underground

SILENCE

Some moments are calling for your silence;
for your stillness and presence. To go beneath
the surface and dive deep, listening to what
this moment is trying to tell you.

✾

TRYING

It's okay to not like where you are now
but still try your best to be happy with it.
(it doesn't mean you like it)

✾

SOLITUDE

The tender silence of being so at ease
in your own company.

✾

SLOWER

A smaller and slower life is no less
meaningful than a fast one.

COMPARISON

Whatever you're feeling right now is okay. If you're grieving, give yourself time to grieve. If you're sad, give your sadness space to breathe. If you're in pain, give your pain the self-compassion it needs. I know how tempting it is to compare your mindset and emotions to someone else's (including my own). But their journey is not your journey. And wherever you are along your path is okay.

I wasn't always this happy and positive; I had so many years where I was angry, sad, lost, and grieving. It took me a long time to transition to who I am today as it is a journey. Happiness, acceptance, self-compassion, peace: all of it is one long, long journey. That isn't to say I got to the place I am today by luck though – it is something I worked incredibly hard for. But it is to say that forcing yourself to feel anything other than what you're feeling, what you think you should feel, or what others in similar situations are feeling, is never helpful.

So remember: your life is your own. Your journey and the pace you're travelling at is your own. Focus on yourself and where you are now. You can still find hope, support and inspiration in other people to help you along the way. But ultimately, this is a solo journey you are travelling on, so everything starts from within.

This might require going through your pain first (like I had to). But that's okay; the key is to remember not to stop there. Don't stay in your tunnel of pain and think that this is the end of your road. There is a light at the end of your tunnel; keep walking until you find it. Don't ever give up. I promise it gets better. And remember that wherever you are along your journey and whatever you're feeling right now is okay.

❄

Please don't compare yourself to someone
whose life you've only stumbled across
when things are good: when they came out
on the other side of their darkness.
You missed the terrible years;
you skipped the monsoon, the earthquake, the fire.
You passed the tears, the anger, the self-hatred.
Understand that behind every story
there are things you cannot see:
there are things you'll never see.
So what you're going through now,
the likelihood is they have gone through it too:
you just never saw it.

Everything is Always Changing

THREE YEARS HOUSEBOUND

There comes a point when the time passed becomes bigger than what the heart can bear. Three years housebound was too much for me. Too heavy to acknowledge, too much time to think about. So I let it pass unnoticed, hoping it might make it easier for me. And in some ways, it did help – not allowing the number three to define me or take up all my focus.

But I realise now I also passed up an opportunity for reflection and growth. A time to see the gained rather than the lost, the gratitude rather than the mourning. To make a list of everything this time has given me and to imagine who I'd be if these three years hadn't happened to me.

Because whenever I feel sad about the time passed, I need to contemplate what my life would have been like if these years hadn't occurred. To take away everything I have learnt; the knowledge, the wisdom, the growth. Because when I do this, I remember that no amount of time can replace what I've gained. The thought of my 'other life' hits home just how thankful I am to have had the chance to become the person I am today. I truly am grateful for these three years.

Underground

CONTEMPLATION

I know it's scary to let go
of the things you cannot control,
but all that energy trying to
change the tide – was it worth it?

❋

INNER PEACE

Inner peace is accepting
how hard things are right now,
whilst holding so much space
in your heart for hope
that things will get better.

❋

YOU'LL GET THERE

You are going to make it.
Wherever you're trying to reach:
you *will* get there.

Everything is Always Changing

SEVEN YEARS ILLNESS ANNIVERSARY

Today officially marks seven years of illness. Seven years to the day when I got glandular fever aged sixteen, which caused the onset of all my ill health. Seven years of a constant, downhill slope in my health, slipping lower and lower each year. Seven years of endless research, study, and experimenting, trying to get better to no avail.

But I won't let all that define these seven years, because goodness knows how far I have come.

I can't, however, turn it all around and say it's also been seven years of a journey towards self-acceptance, peace, and happiness, as that simply isn't true. The first three and a half years were not good: so much resistance, tears, and endless struggle. But the past three and a half years? Yes, those have been a positive, healing journey. A long one, but a very, very good one.

It would be so easy to look back today and be sad about my non-existent recovery. But the thing is, I cannot control when I get better. So why should I judge myself or reflect upon these seven years based on something I have no control over? The simple answer is: I shouldn't. So no, today I'm not going to feel sad about the fact I'm still ill. I have, and I am still doing, the absolute best I can, and that is something to be proud of.

Recovery will come for me one day, and when it does, I can tell you I'll be more than ready for it with open arms. But for now, I'm going to keep living the best life I can possibly live: no matter how small, sleepy, or horizontal it is.

So here's to seven years. Seven years of a long, transformative journey from resistance to acceptance, criticism to compassion, anger to love. And here's to finishing these seven years, lying in my bed, with an endless amount of hope, peace, and happiness in my heart.

Part 2: Emerging

FALSE HOPE

Life is good right now, and that's scary. It's scary because I've been here so many times before. So many times, I've believed this slight improvement could be it. And yet, not once in these past seven and a half years has that belief carried through. Not once has my small sign of improvement been fulfilled and played out. I have always gone downhill. I have always relapsed. Every time, the hope has been taken away from me.

So it's no wonder I'm scared right now. Scared because I've let that hope alight inside of me, giving it a home so close to my heart when the likelihood is it's going to burn me soon. Scared because even though I know I shouldn't dream, given all the past evidence, I'm still allowing myself to believe this could be it. This could be the moment I've waited for. And I'm so scared because if this hope is taken away from me – if I fall again – I can't bear the thought of never getting better, of living a life smaller than I already do.

Should I be living in the moment right now, embracing the better time? Or should I be living with caution? Aware of the likely downfall about to come. Preparing myself for the onslaught of hurt I know could downpour on me at any moment. It's so hard to know which side of the line I should be on. It's so hard to let myself fall, having been so broken-hearted before.

Because what if this is the moment that everything changes – when things finally get better? Is it so wrong to wish for that? Or am I only making the future hurt more painful by holding on to this hope?

I guess the only thing I can do is live in this moment. To try and not compare this moment to previous ones – seeing it as better or worse. To not think about tomorrow or where this moment will lead – but choosing to stay present. Deciding just to *be*.

It's also okay not to want to tell anyone about this moment. To not let others know things are okay right now, as I don't want to confirm that aloud. I'll only have to let them down when my health goes downhill again. It's easier to keep this better moment to myself.

I know there's no point telling others that things are improving, as I have done that before. I have seen the hope and excitement on their faces, only to see it fall as I lose the progress I thought I'd made. Their questions of why and how making it so much harder. So it's easier to stay silent, avoid communication with others, and let this moment of up play out.

Everything is Always Changing

CAR RIDE

So much space,
so much freedom.
My heart drops,
the words fall silent on my lips;
speechless.
To see this view
is too much
for my heart
to take.
So many years of nothing
but walls and enclosure,
and now,
witnessing rolling hills
and endless,
boundless space,
leaves me dazed and speechless.
To describe this moment
is to describe seeing the ocean
for the first time:
no words can justify
how I feel
when the horizon
is nowhere to be seen,
when there is
no end in sight.

Emerging

I just want to run
and chase it down:
seeing how far
this infinite space goes.
I'm struck with awe
at the beauty and vastness
this world offers.
It is a moment
that lingers heavy on my heart.
I feel like I want to cry,
whether out of happiness or disbelief,
it is hard to say.
So many emotions,
running through me at once,
and yet still no words
can form on my tongue.
Speechless,
dazed, awed;
these are the moments that
stay deep inside my heart,
helping me through.
These are the moments
I carry with me
as I go back home
and into bed,
still dreaming of that
endless, boundless space.

Everything is Always Changing

LETTING GO OF ILLNESS-IDENTITY

I realised recently just how much my illness takes up rent space in my mind. It's kind of hard for it not to when it's been with me for so long, and everything I've done for the past eight years has been limited by it.

When I was asked the question, 'Do you define yourself through the perspective of illness?' I wrote the answer: 'Always. My illness is who I am, and it completely defines me. I'm not sure who I am without it anymore.' This answer scared me a lot. And it also made me feel really sad. Have I honestly come to believe so profoundly that my illness defines me and is who I am? And I realise now I do feel this way. I think my illness represents me.

Realising this has made me understand just how much I need to change this belief. I need to find a life away from illness and labels. I need to discover who I am – not solely with these physical challenges I face. But who I am as a person; whole, healthy, and healed.

So this is me saying that I'm ready. I'm ready to start again; to rebuild my identification away from illness. To believe to the core of my soul that I am not my illness and my illness is not me.

Emerging

So here's to starting over. To discovering who I am without illness and learning (or unlearning) that it is not who I am. There is a life to be lived away from these beliefs. I'm so ready to let it all go and discover a new identity.

While you may not be able to shed
the layers of illness when it's
still so present in your life,
you must always remember:
it is a *part* of you,
not the whole of you.
You are what is whole:
your soul, your spirit, your life.
This is your essence.
Illness never was,
or ever will be,
everything
of who you are:
you are so much
more than that.

Everything is Always Changing

THE WAY OUT

And you asked me,
how can I be happy
with all the suffering
surrounding my heart?

Show me the way out,
you whispered.

I looked at you with compassion
and saw the pain in your eyes.
I'm sorry,
I said,
shaking my head,
but I can't tell you that.
Only you can find the
way out of your pain
and back into
the place of love
in your heart.

How though,
you asked,
pleading.

Listen,

Emerging

I replied.
Be still,
seek out the silence within,
and listen.
There is a voice
inside of you,
as gentle as the wind,
trying to show you
the way out:
trying to show you
how to come home to yourself.

Holding your hand,
I said,
don't run outwards
away from it all.
Run inwards,
towards everything you are feeling.

All the answers you are seeking
are already inside of you.
You just can't hear them
above all the noise.
Be still,
and you will hear them.
You will hear the voice
telling you what to do.

THE PRICE I PAID

You're so wise for your age,
they say.

Maybe,
she replies.
But the wisdom earned
came with a price.
A price I wouldn't wish on anyone else.
I am only as wise as I am today
because of everything I have been through.
I'm only *beyond my years*
because I've aged more than I should have;
I'm an old soul who's been through
too much and seen too little.
While I'm grateful for finding
other old souls like myself
to know I'm not alone,
I am also glad
not everyone at my age
is like me.
I'm glad there are people
who act their age
because I know
they still have their innocence.
They haven't gone through things yet

that will change them forever.
So yes,
I'm wise for my age,
but I'm also not supposed to be.
I am who I am
at a price.
So the next time you wish
you could be like me,
remember I am who I am today
because of all I have been through.
You too will become wise someday
when the world is ready
to show you what you need to learn.
Or when you go through something
that shakes you to the core,
and you cannot return to earth
as the same person
you were before.
But until then,
hold onto your innocence
and freedom:
those things are valuable too.

CREATING JOY

I have so many good emotions in my life: gratitude, calm, inner peace, contentment. But what I'm starting to realise is while I have all the 'neutral' feelings, I'm not giving myself enough attention to the joyful moments. To the moments where the happiness is so overpowering, it feels like I'm filled with golden sunlight.

It's not that I'm missing out on these moments. I've just forgotten how essential they are, so I'm not giving myself the time to create them. But I'm starting to see now just how much I need them. How I need times of pure joy, where I could burst with happiness.

So I'm learning to build these moments into my day. I'm consciously putting time aside – even just for five minutes – to laugh, dance, sing, blare music, go to places that make my heart swell – whether in my head or in real life. To do things that make me feel *so* damn happy.

❀

Every day, I'm choosing to reach up and stretch my hands across the skies, smothering them with bold joy.

Emerging

FROZEN

I've been thinking about the fact that while my life has not stopped these past few years, a part of my life did freeze: going out, socialising, dating, being a young adult, the freedom. When I see names of school friends pop up, I know for them, school was years ago. With so many things having happened between now and then. New memories, people, and experiences filling those gaps. But for a small part of me, it literally feels like yesterday as that socialising part of my life has been stuck.

Of course, my life has moved on in so many other directions since then. It's catapulted in ways I could never have anticipated, and I'm so, so grateful for. But I still want to unfreeze that other part of my life. I still want to go back out into the world of socialising and dating, and meeting new people at every turn. Or at least to have the freedom to *choose* to do this.

So while I have moved on in so many ways, there is still a small part of my life that has been frozen since I was eighteen. I feel it the most when people ask me what I've been up to or when school friends catch up on their week. The sudden realisation that while all my memories of me and my friends feel like yesterday, they were actually so long ago.

I can't wait for the day I can move forward with all the pieces of my life. To not leave anything behind. To unfreeze that small part of me that has been stuck. To have the freedom to throw myself into everything and anything I choose to.

And I know it will happen. And maybe it will happen soon. But for now, I'm going to remind myself that it's okay to feel like a small piece of myself is still frozen in time. I have moved forward in every other way possible, and this will help carry me in the future in more ways than I realise.

※

It's okay to feel behind:
to not relate to everything
being said around you.
It's okay to feel
like a part of your life stopped:
because a part of your life did stop.
But also remember,
in that moment when things changed,
so much of your life was born then.
There are things you say and do now

that those around you cannot relate to
because they have not reached
that stage yet within themselves.
There are ways you think
and things you do
that make other people feel behind:
they wish for the growth and learning
you carry now with such ease.

So remember:
it's okay to feel behind
on parts of your life,
it's okay to sit in a conversation thinking,
I can't relate to this.
But also remember:
there are so many things you have now
that other people can't relate to.
And there are also
so many people out there
whose conversation and questions
you can relate to,
because they too
are going through
the same things as you:
you are not alone in
not being able to relate
to the majority.

Everything is Always Changing

LET IT BE

Maybe not everything leaves your life for
a reason, but that doesn't mean it still
hasn't left. So let it go and let it be.

❋

DO IT

I know you're scared,
but please, do it anyway.

❋

DIFFERENT

I know it can be sad to lose a version of yourself you
never thought you'd have to say goodbye to. But that
doesn't mean you're no longer yourself. You're just
different now, and that's okay.

❋

GLOWING UP AHEAD

There are future versions of you that you once
thought were impossible to reach. Look at you glow.

Emerging

LEAVING THINGS BEHIND

When I feel disconnected, lost, or uncertain, I often find myself wandering down stray paths, trying to uncover what it is I need to come home to myself again. I feel the weight of life with each step, the confusion as to why I can't find what it is that I need.

And then I remember – it isn't about what I need, it's about what I need to let go of. To shed the weight of these thoughts storming through my mind and throw them into the wind. To put down the heavy things holding me back. To drop anything that is no longer serving me and to keep doing this, again and again, until that sense of freedom and lightness comes seeping back into my body and soul.

Because when you do this, when you drop everything weighing you down – you realise just how many things you were carrying around with you, trying to bring forwards on this journey. But now you've let them go, the way through seems so easy, so effortless.

You understand now that leaving things behind is often the starting place to finding your way home.

Everything is Always Changing

WORKING THROUGH FEAR

Something I don't think they tell you enough about is how much fear there is during recovery. Fear you'll lose the progress you made. Fear you won't make it. Fear that these months are an anomaly rather than the real thing. Some days it feels like walking on eggshells, wondering if what you're standing on is a foundation or if everything is going to fall through at any given moment.

And then the other thing they don't tell you is how much hard work it is getting through that fear each day. It takes so much effort to wade through it all and come out the other side. To remind yourself you will make it. You will get there. You are getting better. That this is not temporary: it's the real thing.

You have to counteract every fearful thought you have with a positive one. And this takes so much effort. Sometimes it feels like you want to be recognised for how hard you're trying because all the work happens internally: away from what is visible to everyone else.

One way to describe getting through the fear each day is having to think of the happiest memory possible. To let that fill you up until you're bursting with joy. Even though there is so much darkness and heaviness surrounding you, you somehow still have to find a way to think happy thoughts to counteract the fear. This is what it takes to heal – this is what we do every day.

So I want to acknowledge anyone who has to wade through fear every day. I want to tell you: I see you. I see how hard you're trying. I see how much effort it is taking from you. But I also see how it is worth it: it will always be worth it. And maybe, over time, the fear we feel will reduce, and the effort we're putting in will ease little by little. Until one day, we finally reach the shore, and the fear will be no more.

※

I see your silent effort to
relentlessly push past
everything trying to
pull you under.
I see you stepping over
your forests of fear,
untangling yourself
from its branches.

What an amazing
human being you are.

Everything is Always Changing

ENDLESS HORIZON

I made a life within these four walls;
I unearthed peace and happiness,
allowing it to echo off the walls,
bouncing its way into my heart.
And now,
suddenly,
the walls are coming down,
sooner than I can process.
There is so much space
and room.
I don't understand
where to go,
where I should go,
only that I must.

I thought the unknown was frightening:
I didn't realise how much
the open was terrifying.
No walls to keep me distracted,
no survival to keep me occupied.
Just a big wide-open space
and I don't know what to do.

What do I do.
What do I do.

Emerging

What do I do.

Missing the comfort
of confinement
and security,
I go back to bed.
Hiding under the covers
from the vast space
that now surrounds me,
and the wind howling
from miles around,
knowing one day soon
I'll have to journey into it.
But right now,
it's too much.
Right now,
the endless horizon
is simply too fear-crippling.

Everything is Always Changing

LIVING

Now I finally understand what
people meant when they told me
living is harder than surviving.

✳

VICIOUS CYCLE

I'm so desperate
not to repeat old mistakes
that I'm too scared
to take new chances.

✳

I SEE YOU

Look at you, so brave,
carrying on despite the fear – I see you.

✳

DAILY MANTRA

I am choosing to trust the process of
my journey over the visible progress.

Emerging

I MADE IT

Staring up into the deep sky above me,
I still can't get over the fact
I'm here.
I'm not there – inside:
I'm here – outside.
Outside where the air is cold and fresh;
my lungs burning with pleasure,
like each breath
is proof of another chance.
Where there are shoes on my feet
and hills tumbling on my horizon.
Right now,
my head is empty
except for one thought
going around and around:

I made it.
I made it.
I made it.

(Never give up hope
you will make it too).

WALK ALONE

This path I walk
is so lonely
I forget the presence
of my own feet,
supporting me through
the wilderness
as I stumble,
trying to find my way.

This path I walk
is so silent
I forget the absence
of sound is peaceful,
allowing my soul
to speak to me
and be heard.

This path I walk
is so unfamiliar,
I forget the discoveries
that can only be made here,
helping me grow and learn
as a person.

This path I walk

Emerging

is a path I walk alone.
It is lonely,
silent,
and unfamiliar,
but it is also the
way forward:
towards self-discovery
and never-ending growth.

Because sometimes,
you alone
must walk through
the uncomfortable;
the forests of your unknown,
to reach the other side.
To reach the place
that was only
meant for you.
So keep going –
the only way is through.

※

Do not be afraid to do
things alone – some
things are only
meant for you.

Everything is Always Changing

MOVING ON

It makes you realise how far you've come when you think about all the things you used to worry about... what other people thought, grade scores, winning approval, seeking validation, gaining a list of physical achievements to prove your worth.

And yet, nearly all of these things are out of our control and not important in the grand scheme of things.

Now I understand what's important... growth, self-compassion, inner peace, my approval of myself, kindness, happiness. These are the things that truly matter when it comes down to it, and I know I'll always be grateful for learning this lesson.

❋

I've moved on
from seeking
validation
and approval
to seeking growth
and inner peace.

Emerging

I'm grappling with feelings of guilt. Guilt of telling people I'm doing better when there's nothing special about me, no reason I should be improving and not them. I feel like I'm taking my achievements and shoving them in their face, saying, look at me, look at what I can do now, and you can't.

And I know they don't feel like this. I know people see my improvement as a source of hope and joy, as do I for all those I witness on this journey. I know this guilt is within me and not a reflection of the love and support everyone has shown me.

That is the reason I keep telling people I'm improving. It's why I keep writing about it: to fight back against that guilt. To fight back against the voice shaming and criticising me instead of allowing me to be free. To relish in this improvement that I've broken and shattered myself for after waiting so long.

I don't know why I feel like I don't deserve to be completely happy right now. I just recognise the guilt is there. I wish it wasn't. I wish I could scoop up my achievements and shout them from the rooftops and feel nothing but pride. But maybe it's simply a human response. To make excuses for why we're doing well rather than just doing well and enjoying it.

I want to just enjoy it. I know that after these long years, I deserve to feel so far from guilty. To finally feel happy at doing better. I'm going to keep trying to put that guilt aside and soak up the joy. I deserve that...don't I?

Emerging

ROOM FOR IMPROVEMENT

How you start the year does not dictate the tone for how the rest of the year will then be. I started 2019 unable to leave my bed, wash my hair, hold a conversation, or walk further than to the bathroom and back. I ended 2019 spending hours with my friends and family talking, going to Enchanted Christmases and light shows, eating meals downstairs at the kitchen table, joining in with festivities, writing, and going for little walks most days.

So no matter how you start the year, there is so much room for improvement. There is time for things to change and for things to change drastically. Maybe this is your year, or maybe it isn't. Either way, it's going to be someone's year, and perhaps this year that someone could be you. So don't write the rest of the year off as a bad one because it didn't begin as you envisioned. There are still more months to come, and so much can happen in that time.

❋

Even though this year might not have started
off in the way you hoped it would, that
doesn't mean things can't change – there's
still so much time for this year to get better.

SWITCH OF PERSPECTIVE

It's funny how quickly
the joy of recovery
takes away
your worry of what
strangers think of you.
Long gone are the days
walking around in public
buried in my head,
wondering if people
are looking at me.

Now the joy of being out
is blinding,
and it's me noticing other people,
fascinated that they're still real
after all these years.

Emerging

SOCIETY'S VALUES ARE MISPLACED

I can't work out
if the reason
I cannot stop writing
is that
after years
of not being able
to work,
I am making up
for lost time,
or if it's because
I have fallen back
into society's trap
that I am only worthy
when I am producing.
I am only successful
when I sacrifice
my sleep and
healing tools,
crushing myself to the bone,
wondering if now
I'll be valued more.

Everything is Always Changing

NOT NOW

Oh my darling,
why are you still
being so hard on yourself
for resting when your body
screams for you to stop?
Why are you shaming yourself
for not keeping up with the
pace of the rest of the world?
I know you want to know
what it feels like to run so fast,
to chase down the dawn –
the fresh air sweet in your lungs
– but you can't do that my darling,
not right now,
and that is the simple truth.
Maybe one day you can
run with the rest of the world
just to see what it feels like.
But right now, you need to rest
and go at your own pace:
knowing that in your lane
this is what it feels like to run.

Emerging

BE BRAVE

Be brave enough to rest when you need to.

Be brave enough to enforce boundaries with others.

Be brave enough to say no to things you don't want to do.

Be brave enough to say no to things that don't feel right.

Be brave enough to stop when enough is enough.

Be brave enough to put yourself first, again and again.

Be brave enough to walk away from people who don't support your growth.

Be brave enough to recognise your limits.

Be brave enough to honour your limits.

Be brave enough to go at your own pace.

Be brave enough to know your best is enough.

Everything is Always Changing

I am not worth less
just because my body
can't do more.

I am not failing
because I cannot
keep up with the pace
of the rest of the world.

I am not less valuable
because I can't hold
a normal job
or have to rely on
others for help.

I am still worthy.
I am still successful.
I am still valuable.

(and so are you)

Emerging

YOUR PATH ONLY

There is no such thing as the 'right path':
there is only your path.

❋

DESTINATION

Maybe the destination you're
searching for doesn't exist.
Perhaps it's not a specific place,
bur rather, it's your journey
into the wild and unknown itself
that is the destination.

❋

THE STEP BEFORE

Maybe before you find what is meant for you,
you need to let go of what is not.

❋

DAILY MANTRA

I trust in myself and the decisions that I make.

Everything is Always Changing

CAN I SAY I MISS IT?

I miss the comfort of my bed.
Am I allowed to say that?
Am I allowed to admit
I miss the harder life?
I do not mean
I miss the sickness;
plagued by fatigue
with every breath,
the life unknown
outside these walls.
I mean, I miss the simplicity:
the daydreaming,
the absence of responsibility,
the freedom of knowing
you only need to focus
on getting through each day,
and that everything else
must wait.
Because now there's so many
things to think about.

I miss the simplicity,
but I do not miss being there.

Am I allowed to say that?

Emerging

LIFE LOST

Sometimes I wish
for the freedom
and innocence
of the life I lost.
Sometimes I wish
I could take things
less seriously,
feel things less intensely.
But I can't.
Everything I have been through
has meant life is always a bit
heavier for me now,
and that's okay,
as it means I have more room
for joy and meaning too.
While I am grateful for
these last few years –
and I wouldn't take them back
for a moment
– every now and again,
I can't help but wish
I could have the freedom and
innocence back for a little bit
(and I think wanting this
occasionally is okay too).

Everything is Always Changing

DON'T APOLOGISE FOR YOUR EMOTIONS

Please don't apologise for the way you are feeling, whether that's internally to yourself or externally to other people. What you're going through and experiencing doesn't need to be justified with reasons or explanations for why you feel this way.

Sometimes, your emotions just need to be felt, wholly and completely. As often, the easiest way to let them go is to embrace them with gentleness and love first.

❈

By apologising for
how you are feeling,
you're invalidating
your emotions
and experiences.
Please, stop
saying sorry.

EMBEDDED FEARS

When we feel sadder about things than the average person would, it's usually because there's a reason or fear behind our reaction. It's not that we're overreacting – we're just reacting in proportion to our personal history, fears, and perspective. And when this happens, we need to remember to go easy on ourselves. We need to recognise we're doing the best we can.

....

A little while ago, I injured my leg, and I found it so hard to rest up. You see, I've fallen in love with trying to get my body strong again, and going for my ten-minute walk is my daily source of joy. But knowing I was only causing my leg more damage by pushing through meant I was constantly beating myself up for not resting. I kept thinking, if I could rest every single day and not go for a walk once in four years, why can't I manage a few weeks off? Why have I become so privileged in thinking I need to walk to be happy?

I didn't allow myself to complain about my injury because a year ago I would have done anything to have the body I have now. And I know there are so many people who don't have the luxury to go for a walk at all – not even ten minutes.

But then I finally found my self-compassion. I realised this reaction was coming from a place of fear. I started thinking: Why am I not allowing myself to feel sad? After four years of not walking and then four months of having this incredible ability back, is it not surprising that I'm disappointed now it's gone again? Given my circumstances, it's an entirely rational and understandable response, isn't it?

Even though I know this injury and setback is temporary, a lot of the sadness right now is coming from the fear that this isn't temporary. That I'll lose my ability to walk again. So I finally understand that feeling sad about my injured leg is not me overreacting. It's me panicking and covering up the fear that I'll go downhill again.

So in a roundabout way, I want to say: don't beat yourself up for not coping with not-so-significant things as well as you'd like to. There is often a reason and place of fear behind your reaction, and this reason *is* significant to you. Instead of criticising yourself, uncover the worry and cause behind it. Choose to react to your response with love, compassion and gentleness. You're doing the best you can.

Emerging

You think
you can't
get through this,
yet you know
you will survive.

           You think
           this is forever,
           yet you know
           this will pass.

You think
you won't make it,
yet you know
you will get there.

                     You think
                     you will fall,
                     yet you know
                     you will rise.

You think
you can't go on,
yet you know
you'll keep going.

           You think
           this is the end,
           yet you know
           this is just
           the beginning.

Everything is Always Changing

STREET

Everything looks the same
as it did before,
and yet it *feels*
completely different.
Or maybe it's me:
maybe I'm what's different.
Because the streets around me
haven't changed,
but I'm seeing them for the first time.
I'm noticing the details, the people, the colours:
I'm looking up, not down.
I'm fascinated, curious,
by what a single road can hold.

It's amazing how
another mundane street for one
can become a daily source of joy
for another.

(No street or place is ever the same. You're just
choosing to look down and not up. Once you start
looking up, you suddenly realise how much there is to
see that it's literally impossible to take everything in as
there's *so* much see.)

Emerging

THE MAGIC IS RIGHT HERE

Who knew it would take
twenty-four years
to finally fall in love
with my country;
to see all the endless beauty
right here
on my doorstep.

(I'm forever in awe
at all the magic
around me which
I never saw before
when I took
leaving the house
for granted).

❋

There's something
about nature
that always leaves
me feeling
a little smaller,
and yet bigger –
more fuller,
than before.

Everything is Always Changing

IT MIGHT ALWAYS BE A PART OF ME

They tell me to move on, to forget.
But how can I move on
from something
that has been with me
for eight years of my life?
How can I move on,
when these days are
buried under my skin,
etched on my heart.
How can I move on,
when it is still a part of me,
whether I want it to be or not.
How can I move on,
when everything I do,
and will ever do,
started from here.
Because no matter how
much the tree blooms,
it cannot forget its roots;
buried beneath the soil.
And no matter how much
I heal and recover,
I cannot forget the spot
I grew from; marking the
starting place of my new life.

Emerging

When I was nineteen, a couple beside me in a restaurant started chatting to me. They proceeded to ask me what I did, and I had a split-second moment to decide what to tell them. In the end, I chose to lie. I told the couple I was at Bristol University studying Psychology. I knew I'd chosen the 'right' answer, as they were very impressed with this and went on to tell me how intellectual I was.

I've been thinking about this moment a lot and why I chose to lie. I think it was for two reasons. The first is that it's so much easier to lie. My story is not a short one, at least not compared to 'I go to university.' When you're just passing a stranger in life, it feels easier to go with a simple, conventional story that you know they'll immediately understand. But the second reason is that it takes a little piece of me every time I have to tell someone my story and then wait for their reaction. It's not the telling my story part – it's their reaction to my story part that takes something from me.

All too often, the reaction was not good: the conversation always ended up stalling and turning awkward. Or, if it were within a group, I would often get shut out as no one else really knew what to say to me. And this reaction hurt, and it happened to me a lot within the first year of my diagnosis. So that was why I started to lie when strangers asked me what I did.

I haven't had to lie or tell the truth for many years now due to being housebound and not interacting with strangers. But I know I would react differently now. I wouldn't lie to anyone anymore: I'm proud of my story and everything I've gone through. And if my story makes people uncomfortable, then I'm okay with that.

But when I was nineteen, I wasn't okay with it. It hurt me when people judged me for not being at university or having a job. For instead, being a young adult still living at home with a disability. And I know so many other people out there will be, and still are, in that same position I was in when I was nineteen.

So I want to reassure anyone who feels compelled to lie instead of telling strangers their story that it's okay. It's okay to do this. It's understandable, and I've been there and done it too.

But no matter who reacts badly to your story or how many people shut you out because of it, I hope you know that your story is nothing to be ashamed of. There will always be people who want to listen to your story, who will resonate and relate to it. So don't let anyone make you feel ashamed of all the moments you got through to bring you to where you are today. Your story is something to be proud of.

❋

Look at you,
covered in dust,
sweat on your palms,
proof of the deserts you crossed
and the mountains you climbed
to reach this moment.
Look at your heart,
so bold and beautiful,
proof of the magic you uncovered
along the way.
Look at your journey,
so many forest fires
and earthquakes
you were forced to endure,
proof that you survived.
Who wouldn't be in awe
at your story.
Who wouldn't awaken
at your unshakeable strength.
What a breathtaking,
precious human being you are.

Everything is Always Changing

SOME OF IT IS MEANT TO BE LEFT BEHIND

Will the fear always be this heavy?
It's like a continuous reminder
of everything I have been through.
Will I be able to let it go?
Or will the last five years
stay by my side,
like an invisible scar on my heart,
with me for every beat.
I sometimes forget how much
I have been through.
But then I feel the weight
of each breath,
the effort of every step,
of what it takes to
keep looking forward:
to not think about my past
becoming my present again.
Maybe life will always be
a bit heavier for me now.
Or maybe I just need time and evidence
that this improvement
is not temporary but real.
Perhaps I need space to process
the years I spent surviving,
the things I had to do

to stay above water.
But I know now that
every moment I get through
is a moment I can let go of:
Each moment is a chance
to release the heaviness.

(You don't need to carry
everything you have been
through, some of it is
meant to be left behind.)

✻

Wherever you are
along your path,
I hope you remember
you are not alone on this journey.
I hope you remember
someone out there is feeling
what you're feeling,
walking down this road
you're stumbling upon.
Because whatever
you're going through,
someone else is
going through it too:
you are not alone in this.

HIDDEN SCARS

This one goes out
to all those healing
in silence;
behind closed doors
from things
no one knows
they have gone through.
These words are for the people
who keep their battles hidden:
crushed beneath their palm,
hidden amongst the cracks in their skin.

I see you.
Even though I do not know
the things you are going through,
the thoughts you are processing,
the noise you're trying to shut out,
please know, you are not alone.
I see you. You are so brave.
I am rooting for you.
Know that this piece
is dedicated to you.

Emerging

LOOK BEYOND ITS BOUNDARIES

Fear will put walls around you,
but don't let it stop you from
looking out and seeing everything
the world has to offer
beyond its boundaries.

✻

BREAK AWAY FROM THE MIND

How glorious it is to realise
life is bigger than your thoughts.
I hope you have the courage to step
outside of your mind and into reality.

✻

YOU'VE GOT THIS

I know things have been so hard,
but you're doing so well.
Keep going.

NEW JOURNEY

I think that if I get better,
if I'm no longer ill,
I won't know who I am anymore.
I think if I let go of it all,
I will be so lost in this new world.

And the thing is,
I think all that is true:
I will be lost,
but that is also okay.
Because all new discoveries
and beginnings of journeys
start with feeling lost.
They start with nothing:
with letting go and starting over.
And they are so, so scary.
But what we think of
as the end is nearly always
the beginning:
the arrival of something new.
So here's to letting go,
to starting over,
knowing all new journeys
start with feeling
a little lost and scared.

A Conversation with
Wisdom & Joy

Everything is Always Changing

THREE MONTHS PHYSICAL IMPROVEMENT

'Well, this is different,' Joy said, pulling up a chair alongside Wisdom.

Smiling at them both, I replied, 'After everything that's happened this year, it only felt right that you were invited too.'

'Well,' Joy responded, 'I certainly appreciate it. I know how much you've missed out on my presence. So tell me, what *has* been happening this year?'

'I don't even know where to begin,' I answered, bemused. 'Last night I was thinking about all the things I've achieved in the past three months, and I burst into tears. I'm not sure words can convey the joy I feel right now – these months have been everything and more!

You see, ever since I got glandular fever, aged sixteen, I've seen nothing but a steady decline in my health to the point of being left bedbound last year. But this is the first time in my seven years of ill-health that I've had a solid block of improvement – no relapses, no flares, just a little bit up, up and up.

I mean, I'm not spending every minute in bed. I go downstairs each day for a few hours, exploring the world outside of my bedroom. I can cope with more than one person talking in a room, and I'm sitting upright in a chair for an hour. So crazy to do something so normal like sit in an actual chair! I even managed to wash my own hair last week for the first time in nearly two years! I'm sure to some my improvements seem small. But to me, these 'small' improvements are everything. They are huge and overwhelming and liberating.

Saying this out loud is scary, which is why I'm staying quiet about it. The fragility of where I'm at is all too real. I find it easier not to think about it too much so I don't overthink anything. But I also want to share my achievements with loved ones. To hold onto these moments as I've never experienced a solid improvement block like this before.

Of course, there are still many periods of scary ill-health. So I need to document these achievements to give me a light in times of darkness. Because if this isn't pure hope and joy, I don't know what is!'

Everything is Always Changing

FAMILY AND ILLNESS

'My brother came home for a few days last week,' I told Wisdom. 'It got me thinking about how much we often overlook the ways illness impacts loved ones. Because it wasn't just my friends that I couldn't see for over three years: it was my family too. It was my grandparents, my brother, my sister, and to an extent, my parents. Even though they might live with me or know me better than anyone, my illness doesn't give them a free pass.

When my siblings came home, I wasn't able to sit in a room with everyone because it was too much noise. Instead, I would have one visitor at a time in my room – quietly talking on a timer as more than ten to fifteen minutes was too much for my body. Or when my grandparents drove down to see me, twenty minutes was still the maximum. Before my mum got everyone out of the house and off to lunch so I could quietly recover. Even despite all the precautions we took, I still crashed every time I saw a family member. And that was so incredibly heartbreaking.

Heartbreaking because I couldn't spend time with the people I loved. Heartbreaking because for nearly four years, I missed every dinner, every walk, every outing, every photo, every call, every FaceTime. Heartbreaking because I could only hear family updates through my mum as she passed it on in manageable chunks.

I think it's easy to assume even if someone is ill or has severe fatigue, that doesn't apply to their family or household. I would get friends asking if they could see me, not realising I could only see one person a month, and that slot was saved for family. Not realising holidays or events in our house weren't social times for us. They were how many things can we plan *outside* the house so Evie can rest. Not realising it was a continuous, 'You can't come to our house because our daughter/my sister is too ill.'

Of course, there is a light at the end of this tunnel. I had the most amazing few days with my brother home – chatting away and catching up on what felt like years. I can't remember the last time I could sit up and talk to him outside my bedroom. Obviously, I still wasn't able to go out for lunch with my family and had to stay behind to rest up – making the most of the quiet house. But for the first time in nearly four years, I finally got a glimpse of what it felt like to simply be a sister again. And maybe soon, I can move on from being the sick child too, and just be Evie.'

Everything is Always Changing

SEVEN MONTHS PHYSICAL IMPROVEMENT

'I'm enjoying these improvement anniversaries,' Joy said, settling down on the sofa next to me.

'So am I!' I replied, chuckling. 'It's amazing what a difference seven months can make, from functioning at 5% to 30% today. This time last year, I was completely bedbound. I didn't end up leaving my bedroom for 365 days. During that time, every meal and need was brought to me. I didn't make a single cup of tea myself. Showers were a thing of the past. I saw my best friend once that year for fifteen minutes in bed. I had migraine every day and wore sunglasses constantly. All I did was lay in the dark and rest.

Today, I'm going downstairs every day and staying down there for the entire day. I'm able to sit at a table and write. I can shower every third day. I'm baking birthday cakes for people! I've now seen all five of my best friends for the first time in over three years (they kindly came to my garden). I've gone on a handful of small adventures, driving to local open spaces, sitting down on a bench and people watching.

I never, ever thought I'd say this. I never thought I would finally be the one telling others I've improved.

You see, when I was bedbound, I had moments, sometimes hours, sometimes just seconds, where I thought I might never get out of bed again. These moments scared me so much, so I never let them stay. I believed in my recovery, and even now, I will keep on believing as I know it is entirely possible.

All I know is that I never want to forget how much I burst with joy at all these things I can do now. How it feels every morning when I wake up, shower, and go downstairs. And these moments of joy aren't reducing either: every achievement is still as magical and gratifying as the next. But I know it won't always be like this, which is why I want to document this period. I want these words to throw me back in time to this moment where I've been sat crying tears of pure joy simply because I could get my own breakfast. These are the moments I want to hold in my heart forever.

I know I have such a long way to go, but right now, I'm just going to appreciate how insanely far I have come in these seven months. 30% may not sound like a lot to some people, but others will know it is everything to me. This is really happening. After seven long years of decline, I am finally healing.'

Everything is Always Changing

FOUR YEARS HOUSEBOUND

'So I guess I'm taking the lead on this one,' Wisdom said, looking between Joy and me.

'Looks like it,' Joy replied – eyebrows raised – taking a back seat.

'So,' Wisdom said, 'You know the routine, Evie, just tell me what's happening and how you feel.'

Sighing heavily, I responded, 'Today marks four years of being housebound, and now no longer by choice. You see, the day after I left the house for the first time in three and a half years, the UK went into a full lockdown due to a pandemic.'

'Ah,' Wisdom replied. 'Well, I can see why I'm needed here today then.'

'Bit ironic, though, isn't it?' Joy interrupted heartedly. 'You could have picked any other year to get better except the one with the pandemic!'

'Yes, hilarious, Joy,' I responded sarcastically, not exactly in the mood for Joy's humour.

Giving Joy a stern look, Wisdom turned back to me and said gently, 'Go on, Evie.'

'Well,' I responded, 'everything is feeling really strange right now. After sickness has taken a third of my life, I'm finally seeing improvements. So while my world should be opening up, the actual world – or at least the UK – is shutting down. And that's so hard to process. There's a small part of me that feels heartbroken. Yet there's another part of me that's shocked I even want to complain. You know me well enough to know that's not my style; I'm definitely a positive, grateful-for-it-all, silver lining gal. But I guess that only shows how hard I'm taking it.

I know everyone is in the same boat. But for a lot of us, we've been on this boat for years. So while everyone in the world understandably wants to get off it, I want to get off it because it hasn't just been six months for me; it's been four years. And now I finally don't have to be housebound. Or at least I have a chance to be only 90-95% housebound, which is a huge difference from 100%! But I'm not. I'm stuck at 99%, only going for the occasional drive, sometimes stopping at an open green space. The reluctance to want to leave is already huge, given the fear and energy it takes. Then adding the shielding from this virus-thingy on top just makes everything so much harder.

I guess all I'm trying to say is that not leaving the house when you're sick is so hard. And not leaving the house when you're finally healing after years of being housebound, but now you're not allowed to leave, is also incredibly hard.

Of course, I'd rather be here than where I was a year ago. My heart goes out to everyone who is still in that place. And I know I'm grateful in so many ways to have this dilemma; I would have done anything for a problem like this when I was bedbound. I just really didn't want to make it to four years housebound. But here I am. I guess at least I'm no longer 100% housebound, and that's something. I'll take that. It's better than some, and it's more than what I've had in years.'

A Conversation with Wisdom & Joy

SURVIVAL MODE: PRESENT MOMENT

'How is recovery going, Evie?' Wisdom asked me softly.

Pulling out of my daze, I replied, 'A year ago, I was in survival mode. I don't think I knew it at the time, but looking back, I can see it now. Everything was about getting through the next hour. The next minute. The next moment. There were no thoughts of tomorrow or next week because it was a one day at a time mindset.

Now, all of a sudden, I'm finding myself emerging from this survival mindset, and I'm struggling with it. I have so much to process, so much still to heal from. Old patterns are coming back, perfectionism edging in, thinking non-stop, head overflowing. All these things I worked so hard on overcoming are wanting to creep back. And I can see why: my thoughts are no longer of this moment but of the future.

I miss living in the present moment. I miss taking deep breaths. I miss slowing down. I miss just being.

And so this is me vowing to come back to the here and now. To not allow my mind to run away from me. Yes, things are scary out here. Yes, I still worry about the future and money and jobs and never living independently. But no, I don't have to get caught up in this thinking. I don't have to follow society and look ahead: I can choose to look around me. I can choose to come back to taking everything one day at a time. One moment at a time. Just one breath at a time. The worries I have will always be there, but there's no reason I have to listen to them any more now than I did a year ago.

While survival mode was hard, I undoubtedly learnt a lot from it, and living in the present moment was the biggest. So this is me coming back to the here and now, taking a deep breath, and reminding myself it's all going to be alright.'

A Conversation with Wisdom & Joy

'Are we having a party?' Joy asked excitedly.

Laughing, I replied, 'I don't think I'm quite well enough yet for a party – not to mention there's a pandemic going on! But today certainly feels...different. You see, today is my birthday, and it's a big day for me and all those who know and love me. It's a big day because today is the first time I've been able to celebrate my birthday in five years.

When I turned twenty, I was in the middle of a severe crash. I didn't know that the week before when I left the house would end up being my last trip out for nearly four years. When I turned twenty-one, I had the worst migraine of my life. The attack lasted seventy-two whole hours. I was completely paralysed with pain, and it took me nearly a week to open all my cards. When I turned twenty-two, I was happy I got dressed as that was a first for me in three years, but that was pretty much it. When I turned twenty-three, I was completely bedbound. I managed to hold a short conversation with my parents before needing to rest again.

Today I did so many things that I haven't done on all those birthdays previously: I got dressed. I spent the entire day downstairs. I got my own breakfast and lunch. I laughed and talked with my parents. I got to see two of my best friends (the biggest achievement for me). I opened all my presents in one. I had cake. I Facetimed my grandparents and siblings. I even went outside into the garden!

I would be lying to say there's been no sadness building up to this day like there is every year, knowing another year is another year you're still sick. But this year definitely feels different. It feels more like a mourning for the past five years rather than a mourning for the present. Or maybe it's because I still have such a long way to go, and even though it's my birthday, I still have to dedicate most of my day to healing and sleep so I can manage like every other day. But today has definitely been the first birthday in so many years where there's been more hope, happiness and joy than sadness and grief.

I'm still confused over whether I feel nineteen or twenty-four as these past few years have blurred with sickness. But I know I'll definitely remember this birthday. Twenty-four: my first proper twenty-something birthday.'

FRUSTRATION

Wisdom looked at me and said, 'You seem tense.'

Sighing, I replied, 'Something I'm struggling to understand is whether or not I'm allowed to feel frustrated that I still can't do so many things, despite the fact I can now do hundreds of small, everyday things that a year ago seemed unreachable. Because behind every nagging feeling that I'm still missing out on so much, I feel guilty for even having these thoughts. I've got so much more than the year ago me ever did.

But I'm trying to remind myself that while yes, I am doing better, I'm still very sick. So, of course, I'm still missing out on lots of things. I'm just used to comparing myself to bedbound me rather than a fully recovered me that it can distort my perspective on what I can and can't feel frustrated at.

My day-to-day attitude is undoubtedly 99% gratitude and 1% frustration. I feel so privileged to wake up and choose what activity I want to spend my small amount of energy on. A year ago, I didn't have this choice. But there are times when it taxes me how much of my day is still taken up by healing and sleeping. That I only have a few hours left to do the things I actually want to. I'm also experiencing this huge connection between physical and mental energy. It's been jarring to find that if I go for a walk, I'll need mental downtime afterwards.

I think I just need to be gentler with myself and not create this idea that recovery = 100% permanent gratitude. It's okay to feel frustrated that even though I'm improving, 80% of my day is still dedicated to maintaining that improvement. And it's okay to feel frustrated at discovering that while physical activities are something I'm so grateful to do now, it does also suck that it takes all my mental energy too.

I think there's sometimes a view that those who are recovering can't feel frustrated as they've come so far. Or maybe it's a view I've forced upon myself. So this is me just letting myself and anyone else know that whether you're at 1% or 99%: it's okay to feel frustrated sometimes that you're still not at 100%. And that while I feel gratitude nearly every waking moment, I shouldn't be harsh towards myself if I have moments where the exasperation of the effort of recovery gets to me too.'

A Conversation with Wisdom & Joy

EIGHT YEARS ILLNESS ANNIVERSARY

Looking at the photo of sixteen-year-old me in London, Wisdom asked, 'Was this the moment when your life changed?'

'Yes,' I replied, a nervous edge in my voice. 'That was the very moment – exactly eight years ago to this date. It was the day I contracted glandular fever, which caused the onset of my chronic illnesses. I was sixteen then, and being twenty-four now, it means today officially marks eight years of being ill; a third of my life. And truthfully, I can't really remember a time without sickness.

I have so many mixed emotions about this day; so many thoughts I want to share. So I'll just summarise some of the things I'm feeling right now...

❈

Illness is a part of who I am, but it is not who I am. It is a big part of my journey, but it is not my journey.

Eight years of illness is a lot. It's a long time, and it's hard to process the fact that one-third of my life has been dominated by sickness.

Everything is Always Changing

I want to move on from my illness identity and find out who I am away from it all, but it's hard when you're still sick and healing dictates everything you do.

＊

I'm grateful for my illness even if I wouldn't want to repeat it. I wouldn't be where I am today without it, and that's something worth paying for.

I'm not ashamed of my illness or how long I've been sick. I'm proud of my journey and disability label.

I'm not angry or sad for the years it's taken to find all the components for physical healing. I'm just overwhelmed with gratitude and relief that I think I finally have.

＊

You are still healing even when you cannot see the progress. Trust that you are building the foundation and finding the pieces and pillars for recovery: it will show itself to you when it's ready.

If you can't aim for happiness in this moment, aim for peace. Peace is good.

You can be happy and sad. You can achieve acceptance and still grieve. You can practise patience and be frustrated. You can feel awakened and lost. You can feel courageous and frightened.

※

Hope is everything.

Fear is real, but you must keep going beyond its boundaries.

There is life within these four walls: I found it.

There is life outside these four walls: I'm going to find it.'

RECOVERY: AN HONEST UPDATE

'Things seem to have stalled a bit,' Joy asked me tentatively, clearly unsure if Joy or Wisdom was supposed to be speaking right now.

'Yes, they have,' I replied, a little downbeat. 'I've always tried to be as honest as possible with my recovery, so here are two recent developments:

First, I didn't expect a national lockdown to come in two days after I left the house for the first time in over three years. And then for that lockdown to still be in place a year later. I also didn't expect to get injured four months after learning how to walk again, putting me back on bed rest.

Second, I'm okay. At least, I'm putting all my energy and effort into deep breaths, look at how far you've come, it's okay to cry, you're doing so great, stay in the moment, so much joy to feel right here, okay.

Sometimes I feel overwhelmed with joy and excitement at everything I get to do now. Sometimes I cry because of the pain in my leg and the fear my injury and lockdown are stopping my recovery progress. And sometimes – most of the time – I feel like I'm balancing between the two, but spending a lot more time on the 'wow how amazing is life' island.

Did I think recovery was going to be easy? No. Did I think recovery was going to be easier than this? Yes, a little bit. But did I have moments in my seven years of health decline where I thought recovery wasn't going to happen at all for me? Yes.

And yet, look at me! Eleven months of improvement – albeit rather slowly, with a lot of bumps and slopes. But still, improvement all the same. I think, sometimes, you just need to strip back the injury, the lockdown, and focus on one huge fact: I'm doing better than I was a year ago. That's all I need to focus on. That's all I need to hold onto through the obstacles and standstill.'

❋

I must have said these words a thousand times, but that's only because I need to hear them a thousand times: Hope is real. Recovery is real. It can happen to you. It is happening to me.

I'll always keep the torch of hope alight for those of you who are low on yours.

Everything is Always Changing

ONE YEAR PHYSICAL HEALING ANNIVERSARY

'Okay, so I know it's definitely my turn to speak today!' Joy said certainly, seeing the look on my face.

'Yes, it is!' I replied. 'This time last year, I started seeing physical improvements in my health for the first time in seven years. It wasn't much at first. Just being able to open my bedroom blinds a quarter of the way to let some light in. Then, leaving my bed and going downstairs for an hour every few days. Soon the improvements got a little bigger. Staying downstairs for longer and more regularly. FaceTiming family and friends, seeing their faces for the first time in four years. No longer needing to wear sunglasses all the time or plugging my ears when the hoover went off. Then, writing for one hour turned into a whole morning, and then morning and lunch.

Even though my recovery has stalled a bit in 2021, mainly due to my injury, winter, and lockdown, I have come such a long way in a year. So today, I am celebrating one year of remission. One year of beginning to reverse the other seven. One year of travelling along the path of visible physical healing. One year of starting a journey of self-discovery outside of these four walls and my illness label.

One thing I will say, though, is that this past year has *not* been the year of 'finally living' or 'getting my life back.' I still had a life when I was at my worst. I still had meaning when I was bedbound. I was still living when my world was confined to one room. My life was just as meaningful and valuable a year ago as it is today.

Don't ever let yourself believe or let others make you believe that you're only 'living' when you're improving. Or that you only have meaning when you can do things. Because I promise, no matter how big or small your world is, how much or little you can do: You are still living a life that is meaningful and valid. You *are* still living.

This celebration today is not a year of getting my life back. It's celebrating a year of finally seeing the physical healing I worked towards for seven years. It's celebrating all that trust I put into believing I was healing – even when I couldn't see the visible progress – paid off. It's celebrating beginning a new path, a new journey, and a continuation of self-discovery and healing.

Happy one year of visible physical healing to me.'

YOU WILL GET BACK UP

'It's been a rough few weeks,' I said to Wisdom. 'I remember six months ago when I made it to the field down my road, and I was in awe. No words could express what it meant to be able to walk there by myself for the first time in four years. I actually made it. I cried. I laughed. I genuinely couldn't believe it was real!

A month ago, after ten weeks of bed rest due to an injury, I made it back to the same field. Except, this time, the accomplishment was smaller in my mind. I was so focused on my leg – *Was I overdoing it? Was I straining the injury? Did it hurt?* I lived so much in my head that it bypassed me to stop and realise, once again, I had been knocked back. And yet, once again, I had made it. It didn't matter that this time took ten weeks compared to four years previously; I still made it. I still made it against the nagging worries that I wouldn't.

Today, after two weeks of being very ill, I made it to the field again. And this time, I went with the perspective like the first. The relief that I got through these two weeks, and better still, made it to the field, was as overwhelming as making it after four years. The fear that I would relapse and not recover made it a walk of pure joy and relief. Just so grateful with every step and breath that the fear hadn't come true.

Reflecting upon these same achievements repeated within six months reminds me of something important. It reminds me that no matter how many times my mind tells me I won't make it – whether it's been four years, three months, or two weeks – my body has proven itself to me again, again, and again. While there's some evidence to say I'll get worse once more, there's more proof (plus hope and belief) to say I won't – that these setbacks are temporary. And even when I do get knocked down – which I keep reminding myself is inevitable – I still get back up each time.

I'm so relieved these past two weeks are over. But more than anything, I'm proud I got through them. And prouder still, I bounced back to my baseline quicker than expected.'

❋

I hope that whatever is knocking you down right now, whether it's been years, months, or weeks, you too can remember you will get through this, you will get back up again. And remember, when you do, stay in the moment and celebrate your achievement!

STILL VALUABLE

'I think society has its values backwards,' I told Wisdom.

'What do you mean?' Wisdom responded.

'Well, society makes me feel less valuable because I live in a body that can't do as much as my peers. I was only seventeen when my health forced me to drop out of school. I left with no A-levels, went to no university, hold no degree, no job. And for some reason, society deems me less valuable because of this.

Some of the first questions people often ask upon meeting are: 'What do you do for a living?' 'What university did you go to?' 'What's your job?' While I know this small talk is natural in our society, it's hard when you have no answers to these questions. It's hard when you know success is decided on what's on a piece of paper rather than what's in your heart.

I know not all of society is like this. I'm so grateful for the people I have in my life who never make me feel less valuable than them. But that doesn't change the fact I often feel this way about myself, and I know a lot of this is due to what I've absorbed from society. So

I'm still unlearning these things. I'm still unlearning what success means. I'm still unlearning that working every night until midnight is less important than how I treat myself and others. I'm still unlearning that being disabled with no qualifications doesn't mean I'm not clever, ambitious, or incapable of learning.

But I know it's going to be an ongoing, daily job of unlearning. I know that as I become part of society again, I'll have to grapple with all these questions once more. And the reality is, I know if I tell someone I don't have a job or even A-levels, some people will immediately place me as 'lower' to them. But I also know the harsh truth that if I then tell them I've written a book, they might place me back on the 'successful' list. And I don't want that. I don't want to use my achievements to make others see me as worthy.

I am just as valuable today even if I hadn't written a book. I am just as valuable if all I had done up to this point was survive. And I know that those who are kind and deserving of my time will never make me feel any less valuable than them, ever.'

Everything is Always Changing

DON'T EVER GIVE UP HOPE

Standing in the middle of the park, with the beautiful red and orange leaves littering the floor – evidence of the changing season – I turned to Joy. I said, 'Exactly a year ago today, I posted a picture of this precise spot. At the time, I was too poorly to leave my bed. So my dad had taken the photo for me on his walk so I could see some of the outside world. In the caption below the picture, I wrote:

'I wish with all my heart I could say I took this photo. That I made it 'out there' to witness the beautiful scenery that surrounds us at the moment. To look up into the vast blue sky, my feet on the ground, the wind in my face.

But right now, I can still only witness the changing of another season through photos people post and my family and friends send me.

I won't give up hope, though, that I will get to see it all through my own eyes soon. I won't give up hope that all this effort I'm putting into getting better will pay off. I won't give up hope that I'll start to feel better any moment now. And I won't ever give up hope that I will be able to leave this house and go off and do all the things I dream of very, very soon.'

One year after posting this caption, I achieved everything I'd been dreaming of in that moment. I saw the changing season through my own eyes: I witnessed it for myself. I went outside, walked amongst the leaves, felt the wind on my face, and looked up into the expansive sky.'

Whatever you're wishing for right now, don't you give up hope on that either. Dreams really can come true.

Part 3:
Blooming

Everything is Always Changing

WITNESSING MY PROGRESS

What a beautiful thing it is
to look at the words I wrote
at the beginning,
in the underground,
and see all the hope and trust
I continually poured into my soul
that I would make it
blossomed into truth.
How breathtaking to witness
that bedbound me
would find the words on the page
became the story of her life
within such a short space of time.

I am honoured
to have a front-row seat
into my growth
and progress.

Blooming

HAPPINESS KEEPS EXPANDING

I often look back to my first year of being housebound and think, *was I as happy as I made out to be?* I almost belittle my past self for acting happy, not believing I could have been. But I was happy back then. I just didn't know at the time how much more my happiness could grow and expand. I didn't realise how wide and expansive my feelings could become. Because, in that moment, I had reached the summit of my happiness – I was at my highest point.

Now, four years later, my happiness peak has risen higher than I could have imagined. So when I compare my past happiness to today, it looks small to me now. Compared to today, everything I previously felt is so far off the scale from what I now know is possible.

I'm sure when my happiness peak has climbed even further in a few years, I'll look back on this time too and think, *was I as happy as I told everyone I was?* Because that is the thing with happiness: every time you think you've reached the highest point, you keep on climbing. You keep diving further into its depths.

So while I feel I am at the highest point right now, the reality is there is still a mountain above me. And knowing that how I feel right now is only a slither of my happiness potential gives me so much hope for the future. I understand now that this is not the highest point I can reach in life – it's just the highest point in this moment.

※

And when you feel
you can go no further –
that you have reached
the end of the road
for your happiness journey:
look up my love,
and see the mountain of possibilities
climbing high into the skies.
Don't let it scare you – no,
let it rage an earthquake
of courage and hope within you,
knowing there is
a future you up there
looking down, smiling, thinking,
she has no idea of all the good things about to come.

Blooming

A BEND OF THE HEART

Sometimes the things we seek
are maybe not as far away
as we think they are.
Maybe all it takes
is a bend of the heart,
a change in the soul,
to discover everything
we were missing
was only a breath away
from the spot
where we were standing.

EVOLVE PAST THEM

On your journey of
self-discovery and growth,
you'll reach a crossroad
where you have to choose
to evolve past those around you
or to stay where you are:
I urge you to keep going.
This is your journey, not theirs;
there is no barrier here for you.

LET IT OUT, LET IT GO

Oh my darling,
why are you resisting
these emotions
swirling inside of you?
Let them rise up
and spill out,
like waves crashing onto the shore.
Let them break loose,
because only when
they are free and flowing
can you let them go.
Don't give your emotions the power
by bottling them under.
They are not meant
to be caged inside of you:
your feelings are not yours to hold.
They are fleeting
and forever moving:
this is their natural state.
So release them from your hold,
knowing this is how it should be.
Let them out my darling,
let them out,
then let them go.

Blooming

Coming home from spending a day with friends, I find myself more emotional than ever, and I'm not sure why.

I think I'm feeling sadness for the girl I was. The one who missed out on so much for so long. Who now starts every sentence with, 'When was the last time I did this?' 'It's been at least five years.' The girl whose last memories in the real world were when she was nineteen. Now in her mid-twenties, a lifetime seems to have gone by, and yet nothing seems to have changed.

But I also feel sadness for the girl I am. Suddenly realising the heaviness of these past few years are like a weight on my heart. Sad because a day with friends still means in bed by 7pm to compensate: the days after put aside to recover. Sad because I want to do this all the time. I want to always be out, to never have to come home. Yet knowing this isn't the reality. I'm still tied down, bound with an illness I've held hands with for so long. Allowing me some freedom, but not enough to make me forget for too long that my life is still so different and restricted.

Everything is Always Changing

And I feel sadness for the girl in the future: the one who has to contend with the unknown. The constant questions of, 'Will the trips out always take this much energy?' 'Will I ever fully recover?' The money worries, the becoming-independent struggle, the identity crisis.

But I also know this:
while I can only feel the
sadness right at this second,
this is not a true reflection of my
past, present, or future.
Because there is pride of the past:
getting through the moments
I'd never thought I'd get through,
finding happiness and life alongside illness.
There is joy in the present:
relief at finally improving,
all-encompassing happiness at
seeing loved ones and walking in the outdoors.
And there is hope for the future:
a belief and trust that if
I've worked everything out so far,
then I will work out my future too.

I won't let this temporary moment of sadness
distort how I truly feel about my life.

HEAVY MORNING

Sometimes it's easier when you wake up and your emotions are heavy: the sadness clinging to you like honey. It feels easier in these moments to know you must do something about it. Understanding that today is a day of prioritising self-care and compassion.

Because when it's not heavy enough to dominate your heart – when the sadness merely lingers in the background – it's easy to brush it aside. It's easy to think: *I will deal with you later.*

So I'm grateful for the mornings when my emotions are heavier: gripping me so tightly that I have no choice but to take notice – making me surrender to their weight. I know on these days that I must move with a gentleness and grace. I must do my best to create space for the heaviness, forcing its way through.

And for the mornings when the weight is still there but not present enough for me to stop: I hope I can pause. I hope I can be gentle enough with myself that the load doesn't keep building until I *have* to notice it. I hope I can find that middle ground where I recognise I'm not quite myself and honour the moments of silence and stillness I get until I feel myself again.

Everything is Always Changing

THOUGHTS ON HEALING

Healing is both messy and beautiful. Liberating and hard.

You will outgrow some of the people you love.

Healing is the best and bravest thing you will ever do.

You don't need to explain the way you choose to heal to anyone.

Crying is inevitable.

While healing is ultimately a solo journey, you don't have to do it alone.

Self-help books can be life-changing.

Holding on hurts more than letting go.

Healing is not a journey you come back from: it's a never-ending road of discovery and growth.

There is no time limit when it comes to healing: take as long as you need.

Blooming

THE POWER OF SHARING VULNERABILITY ONLINE

Every time I think
I am the only one
having these feelings,
I pour them out
onto my little white screen,
clicking share,
only for my comments to explode with
I thought I was the only one,
you've explained exactly what I feel,
you've taken the words out of my mouth.
How funny it is
that there has never been a time
when someone has not said
me too
to the words I've shared.
And yet I still think
there could be a chance,
with seven billion people in the world,
that I am the only one
feeling this way.
I am not,
and neither are you.

Everything is Always Changing

FELT

Words cannot always explain
why the heart feels
the way it does,
but only that it does.

(poetry doesn't need to
make sense, only felt)

❋

THE ART OF POETRY

All this pain tucked away
in the folds on my skin;
I take it and put it onto paper,
transforming it into
something beautiful.

❋

CONNECTION BETWEEN US

I write and share the words
I need to hear in the moment,
and the fact they resonate with you too
is a beautiful thing to me.

Blooming

So much fear
surrounds my heart
as I seem to be stumbling
through the wilderness
more than ever.
So many possibilities opening up,
yet everything so blank
at the same time.
The emptiness is exciting
as it is terrifying.
I know it'll be hard,
I know it'll be scary,
but I also know,
in so many ways,
it can't be half as hard
as what I'm leaving behind.
I don't know where I'm going,
I don't know what I'm doing,
but I'm just grateful
to finally be able
to look forward.

Living.
Not just surviving.
And while living is so damn hard.

Everything is Always Changing

I will do it.
I will do it for the person I left behind.
I will do it for myself because I have to.
Those years weren't for nothing.
They were for this.
And now I have to keep going.
Where?
I don't know.
Will it be scary?
It'll be terrifying.
But I have to do it.
I have to know where this road goes
and the never-ending journey
I'm being taken on.
I have to keep moving forward,
for me.
Despite the fear,
I have to keep going.

Blooming

I NEED TO BECOME SOMEONE ELSE

The thing is,
despite my change
in circumstances,
I'm still the same person
I was in my room:
I didn't leave her behind.
But I also know
the girl from my bedroom
is not the person
I need to be
out here
in the open world.
The girl in the bedroom
was all about survival;
about breathing,
about one step at a time.
But the girl I need to be
out here
is more complex.
She needs to survive,
but live.
She needs to breathe,
but move.
She needs to take things
one step at a time,

whilst working out
where those steps might be.

I don't know whether
the person I need to be
out here
in the big wide world
is harder than
the person I needed to be
within those four walls.
But I do know that
I became the person
I had to be
inside my bedroom,
and I will become the person
I have to be
out here.

I AM becoming her.

Blooming

RUSHING FOR WHAT?

Why are you breaking yourself in two to achieve something that won't ever be worth the breakage it took to get there. Why are you sprinting tirelessly towards this goal *you* have created in your mind, one with time limits and maximum speed. What happened to the purpose of being happy? What happened to the pursuit of *living*. Do you not want that too? Because you can have both: you can still live and love, smile and laugh, *and* run towards the things you desire.

But you don't need to run so fast that you drop everything in the process. You don't need to sprint yourself into exhaustion, forgetting it's okay to stop or walk the whole way at a leisurely pace. Unless you see that your life is only ever now – in this moment – and not in your pursuit, can you remember your goals can be *anything,* but they cannot be *everything*. There must be more to your life here than far ahead. So yes, keep looking up at the horizon, but please remember to look around here too: there is no rush.

❄

Even if you achieved
the result you wanted

Everything is Always Changing

at the end of all this rushing,
was it really worth
all that heavy heartedness?
The restlessness, the lost sleep,
the poor connection with loved ones,
the lost communication with yourself,
running endlessly on no steam.
Was one moment of achievement
worth the sacrifice it took to get there?

Or perhaps,
would remembering
to live, sleep,
spend time with loved ones,
spend time with yourself,
along the way of this pursuit –
even if it takes you longer –
would this path not be better?
It is not a slower path;
it is a fuller path,
with balance, life and joy.
This is the path to take.

❋

Here's to those of us relentlessly remembering
the reckless act of slowing down
in a world so encouraging to speed up.

Blooming

EACH ONE AS IT COMES

Growth is not linear.
So don't put pressure on yourself
after coping well with
a particular situation or emotion,
to cope well with *every* same
future situation or emotion.
You don't overcome something once,
then it's always easy.
The likelihood is
you will have many more times
where you fall at the same spot
you thought
you'd just got through.
So take each hurdle as it comes:
see it as an opportunity
to discover what you can learn
from the process
this time around.
Don't measure your growth
on the outcome
or expect yourself
to have fully conquered
this obstacle.
Growth is an ever-changing journey,
not a tick box exercise.

TO-DO LIST

You think you're not doing enough.
You think you're not trying hard enough.
That the reason you cannot complete
your to-do list is on you.
But it's not.
You're simply asking
too much of yourself:
you created a to-do list
that was unachievable.
You can try as hard as you like
(which you already are),
but it's not you: it's the list.
It's too long, too much for one person.
You're expecting too much of yourself,
no – you're literally expecting the impossible.
So the next time you ask yourself,
am I doing enough?
Don't look within
but look without.
The likelihood is
you are trying hard enough.
You're just asking too much of yourself.
That is why you constantly feel
like you're never doing enough
because you're always trying to achieve

more than you'll ever be able to do.
So stop asking
if you're doing enough
and understand there is only
so much one person
can do in a day.

(Question your expectations and
the length of your to-do list,
not yourself.)

Everything is Always Changing

MISSING YEARS

It hits you.
When someone asks your age,
and your tongue forms the words
twenty-one
before you realise
you're three years out:
you're twenty-four.
It hits you that
so many years have been given
to illness and sick health.
The loss and grief
spring up from seemingly nowhere.
You wish you could get those years back,
but you also really, really don't.
It's a strange sensation,
being overcome with grief and realisation
at how much time has passed,
but that you still treasure those lost years.
They built you into
this person you are today,
and you're so proud of that.

I don't wish I wasn't twenty-four.
I just wish, sometimes,
I could feel like it.

Blooming

LEAN TOWARDS IT

And through the weight
of this sadness
clouding over me,
smothering me like a blanket,
I'll wrap myself up in it,
embracing the weight,
and find solace in the softness
of acceptance.

THROUGH

When you embrace your
heavier emotions,
make sure to go
all the way through:
to feel them all the way.
There is a light
on the other side.

Everything is Always Changing

One day you will suddenly realise: all those little things you used to get worked up over no longer affect you.

You respond to situations with calm and clarity when years before you would have responded with anger.

You notice you've stopped comparing yourself to others and understand that your journey is *yours* alone.

You see that the things that matter to you the most now are the little joys: you don't rely on the big things.

You've come to believe in yourself and who you are – the days of criticising or belittling yourself are in the past.

And all this time, you were wondering if you have made any progress; if you had reached the stage of awakening. But it turns out you got there long ago. It's just now you notice how far you have come.

It's only now,
you can suddenly see,
how much
you've changed.

Blooming

NOTES OF GRATITUDE

Not all forms of
profound gratitude come
from life-changing events
or extraordinary moments.
Sometimes,
stockpiling notes
of all the mundane
and ordinary things
that have brought you
tiny moments of joy
throughout the day
lead you to that place
of deep and
enduring gratitude.

❋

EXPAND

The beautiful thing
about gratitude is that
the more you feel it,
the bigger it seems
to expand.

Everything is Always Changing

TO THOSE I LEFT BEHIND: I SEE YOU

I feel others pain and sickness so deeply. When I look back and see how far I've come, I feel a stab of sadness at all those I've left behind. Those who are still as sick as I was a year ago, trying to get better to no avail.

One of the heartbreaking things about recovery is that you can't bring everyone else forward with you. My heart hurts when I overtake someone who has been struggling for years. Or someone else who is still stuck in that place I was in.

It's not a comparison thing; it's a pure compassion thing. I wish I could make everyone better. I wish I could hold everyone struggling. I wish those who are sicker than me now, or have seen no improvement in years, knew how much I think of them.

Sometimes teeny feelings of guilt creep in: why am I getting better and they're not? I've done nothing special. I'm trying just as hard as everyone else. But I can at least take comfort in the hope that my progress and healing can show you it's possible. That because there is nothing special about me or my recovery, there's no reason you can't recover too.

Blooming

So whoever needs to hear it: I see you. Even though I'm going forward, I won't forget all those still behind me or stuck in the same place.

I'm going to make it: and so will you. We'll all get there, and we'll get there together.

Rooting for you, always.

GRIEF

And the word for what I've been feeling finally comes to me: grief. Grief for the past four years. Grief for the girl I was. Grief for the years I've spent surviving. Grief for the time slipped through my hands.

I thought I was done with grieving. I thought I had accepted what's gone, the life lost, and embraced my new one. But maybe it was easier to accept the grief when the environment was so different; when nothing around me felt familiar. But now that I'm out in the world again, the grief is hitting me with full force. Memories at every corner, places I'd been to and haven't in four years. So much grief processing the time between now and when I was nineteen.

I've heard people say grief is messy, but I think I'm only just beginning to understand that. I'm only just understanding you can think you've healed from something, only to find – years down the line – there were layers still to come. It wasn't that you missed them or that you weren't fully healed; it's just there were more stages for you to go through.

And now I'm going through stages I wasn't prepared for, and until now, I hadn't thought of the word grief.

Blooming

But that is the word; I know it is. I am grieving. It's why my heart is heavy and I cry out of nowhere.

But I hope that now I know what this is – that this thing I'm going through is grief all over again – I can be more prepared for it. I can notice when it arrives and sit down with it, letting it breathe and run its course. And I can make the most of the soft moments in-between when the grief quietens down, enjoying the long stretches of acceptance and calm peace.

Placing a hand over her heart,
she breathes in the quiet
self-compassion, soaking up
the tender love through
her fingertips, as she remembers:
healing is a never-ending process,
I can reach a place of acceptance
and still bring grief along with me,
I won't always feel this way,
this feeling is not forever.

Everything is Always Changing

TORN

I am constantly torn
between wanting to run and
create a new life for myself,
and staying behind to build
back up parts of my life
my illness broke.

❄

LOVE LETTER TO MYSELF

I know you're scared,
but I believe in you,
and I know you can
get through this.

❄

GO FORWARD FROM THIS MOMENT

What if we stopped
moving forward with
the steps of our past,
and instead, started
where we are.

Blooming

And even when those around you
think you should be
so happy right now,
that you're living the dream,
but you can only feel
the heaviness of the past,
the fear of the future,
I want you to remember
it is normal to feel this way.
You cannot expect
to move forward and
let go as easily as they say.
You need the time
to process, heal,
change, evolve.
And you can take as much time
as you need to do those things.
Your mind cannot recover
at the same rate your body can.
Be easy on your mind:
let it go at its own speed.
You'll heal, in your own time,
your own way.
Trust the process of it
over the progress.

DRAINED

No wonder you're struggling darling. Can you not see how drained you are? Can you not feel the weight on your heart? You're giving out when you have nothing inside. You're drained, completely and utterly. Stop giving away drops you don't even have.

Come. Come back to me. Come back into yourself and dive into your soul. What's happening, my love? Why do you feel so empty? Have you been running for too long?

Stay. Stay here for a while. Stay and replenish your heart. Turn off the outside world. You are no use to them if you cannot even give enough to yourself.

Breathe. Breathe love into your body and mind. You've neglected them too long. Give them the attention they deserve. Put them first. Talk to them. Hear what they are trying to tell you.

Wait. Wait here until you feel ready. When, you say? You'll know. You'll know when you're ready to face the outside world again. Now you're back in touch with yourself, you'll feel when it's too soon. It'll probably take longer than you hope. But whatever you do, don't cut off that communication again. Don't fall into this cycle of give and no take.

Stay full, my love. Then, maybe then, you can give. But not a second before. And whatever you do, don't give out unless you're giving in to yourself too.

❋

PEOPLE PLEASER

Even the moon and sun
take it in turns
to shine.
Stop thinking
you can shine
all day long.

Everything is Always Changing

THE GUIDE IS WITHIN YOU

How courageous you are,
stumbling forwards
into the blankness
with no pages written
or pictures drawn.
How beautifully
you're wading through
your unknowns,
with no guide to follow,
no one to give you
knowledge of what's up ahead.
How incredibly
you're creating your own path,
with nothing
but the weight on your heart,
the freedom in your soul,
and the stories on your back.

Because what else do you need to go forwards? You
carry a world within you. Embodied in every heartbeat
is the weight of an entire universe, helping you,
whispering to you. So remember, even though you
have no one else to guide or follow you down this path,
you already have a world within, ready to go with you,
wherever you turn.

Blooming

MIGRAINE ATTACK

This pain will cease.
This storm will pass.
Keep holding on
and breathe gently
through it all.

※

BELIEVE

I don't know what
the future looks like,
but I'm going
to be okay.

※

HAVE FAITH

Some things are meant
to be done quickly and
some are meant to take longer:
trust the process of both.

Everything is Always Changing

STANDSTILL IS A PRIVILEGE

Am I stuck, unable to move forward?
Is this it: is this as far as I can go?
Can my body carry me no further?
Why has everything slowed.
Is this meant to happen?
Am I meant to have a middle point:
a standstill until the barrier lifts
and I can move forward again.

Realisation dawns on me –
right as I'm putting the pen on paper
to write these words.
When did I stop focusing
on the fact I'm not going backwards?
Seven years and my health did
nothing but go backwards.
Goodness how I realise
I'm looking at this all wrong.
Standing still is a *privilege*.
While I'm uncertain
if I'm still moving forward,
I am confident
I am not moving backwards
– and that,
that is something,

Blooming

isn't it?
What I would have given
to say even those words
for so many years.

So here I came to write about my pains,
only for the words to be already prepared
to teach me about my privilege.
To see it with such shock,
I feel so lucky to be stuck where I am.

The barrier will lift,
and I will move forward once again.
But if I'm going to be stuck anywhere,
this is a pretty good spot.

Enough time to adjust
to the rapid changes of last year.
Enough space to gather
my courage and strength,
ready for the next stage.

Everything is Always Changing

THIS PAUSE IS FOR YOU

Maybe this standstill
is not about me
not improving anymore,
but my body recognising
my mind cannot keep up
with the rapidly changing speed.
Maybe this is my body saying:
here,
let's pause *here* for a while.
As wonderful as this
improvement has been,
I know you've struggled
with the rapid changes.
So let's stop
and give you a moment
to find your footing,
to gather your strength,
to realise just how far you've come,
to pick up all the healing tools
you dropped in the rush.
And then,
once you feel ready,
we'll set off again.

Blooming

You are stressing out over things
you'd normally be calm about
because your heart is heavier
and your thoughts
more tumultuous
at the moment.
Stop criticising yourself
for not coping
with something
as well as you think
you should be.
You are doing
the best you can.
Be gentle with yourself.
Know that your reaction
to the same scenario
will differ each day
depending on how you feel.

Don't expect to be
the same every day
because *you* are not
the same every day.

WRONG CHOICE

When it comes to deciding which path to go down, which door to go through, there is no such thing as the 'wrong choice.' This is because you can never know the route you would have taken other than the one you took. Even if you feel you chose wrong afterwards, that feeling itself is proof you have learnt something from this path. And you will take that lesson with you for future decisions.

Because each door in life is a door filled with opportunities to learn and grow. So even if you are given a hundred doors – and you're struggling to know if the one you're about to choose is the right one – walk through it with confidence, knowing there is no such thing as the wrong choice. And even if you wish you could go back and enter a different door, take a different path, hold on to the trust that more opportunities will be presented to you in the future. There will be the chance to try again.

So don't criticise yourself for the choices you made in the past. You only did what you thought was best with what you had in front of you. And you're still only doing your best today. You cannot foresee the consequences of these choices. You cannot peek into the future to see if you will look back on this moment and think, 'Did I make the right choice?' You can only work with what you have now, and that is always enough.

※

And even with
the maze of paths
surrounding me,
never knowing which one
is the one
I'm supposed to take,
I will take comfort in recognising
it's okay to feel disheartened
and disillusioned,
not understanding which way to go.
It's okay to falter,
overwhelmed with the options.
But I will trust and believe
that when I do step forwards,
I am making the right choice for me,
even if I cannot see it.

(even the wrong paths
can help lead us
to the most beautiful
destinations)

Everything is Always Changing

CURIOUS

I hope you find the courage
to follow your curiosity
and find out where
this path leads.

※

THIS WAY

You can move forward
without having a clue
where you're going
or why you feel
that *this* way is your way,
only that this *is* the way.

※

LETTING GO

The irony of letting go:
you always gain more than you lose.

Blooming

The realisation that I am qualified
for nothing, to go nowhere,
is being made starker than ever.
All I have are these words
clawing at my skin,
begging for their way out;
to be released into the open air.
Rising up my throat,
I feel them pouring from my lips
and out onto the page.
They find their air
here in the ink.
I cannot hold them in:
I must keep them coming.
I will die inside
if I do not free them.
They are how I can breathe.
Keeping them inside,
I only allow them to weigh me down.
But seeing them on paper,
I finally uncover everything
I was trying to keep hidden.
Letting them up and out,
I am finally free to
breathe a little easier.

Everything is Always Changing

Starting over somewhere new
won't solve your internal problems.
But also know it's okay to crave
a new external environment
after so much inner work.

One where your old self isn't
reflected through memories
on street corners and places
you've already been,
filled with people
who knew you from *before*.

It's okay to want a clean slate:
to take this new perspective with you
and run towards a fresh start
where no one knows your name.
Where you can learn
who you really are
with this newfound mindset,
without memories of the past,
and go somewhere
untainted and new.

Blooming

When you feel lost and disconnected, it's easy to run away from your emotions. It's easy to keep putting more and more distance between yourself and what lies within. Even if you know you must embrace your emotions, too many years of fleeing make this normal. It's familiar for you to run instead of stay.

But you're only making it harder to connect by hiding. You're only getting yourself more lost. So when you realise you've been burying your genuine state, choose to go within instead. Go beneath the layers of life and everyday thoughts and run directly inside. Plant your feet in this earth and sink into yourself until you find that unshakeable life and belonging within.

It might take a lot of dropping everything and fleeing inwards until you unearth that feeling of connection. Until you shed the layers of feeling lost. And you might have to keep doing this. To keep folding inwards, again and again. But you will come home and find yourself once more. You will come back into the moonlight within and look up and see the light inside of you all along.

Everything is Always Changing

SELF-DISCOVERY

There is a place inside of you
that you have never visited.
Go to that place,
and never return.

✳

EVOLVING

I want to grow so much
that a year from now
I won't recognise
the person I am today.

✳

FOREVER SEEKING GROWTH

And little by little,
I aim to become a
better person
than the one I was
a few moments ago.

Blooming

It hits me all over again
how much I'm still
missing out on.
Twenty-four years
I've grown up in the
same small village, never
to have flown the nest.
Will my world always be
limited: bigger than it was
to make me feel guilty
for wanting *more*,
but smaller
than everyone else's,
to remind me
it's still not *normal*.
Limited – is this what
I should get used to?
A life with fences;
tantalising close to
the sweet open-air,
but only enough to *taste*
the freedom on my tongue,
but never enough to *feel* it
within my body and soul.

Everything is Always Changing

WHAT THEY DON'T TELL YOU ABOUT RECOVERY

Recovery is like
constantly trying to breathe
in a sea of fear
that this isn't real:
that this is all to be
taken away from you,
just at the moment when
you finally believe
it might stay.

Recovery is wondering,
if I jump off the ledge
into the world out there,
will I soar and fly,
my buried wings
finally hatching?
Or will I fall and crash?
Only to have further to climb
back to the beginning.

Recovery is fighting
every damn day
with the alienness of it all:
shops, people, life.
After so long,

Blooming

trying to remember,
you used to do this
all the time when you were a kid,
this used to be your world:
this *is* your world now.

Recovery is trying
to hold on to the lessons
you learned from the past years,
clinging to them
like petals in a storm,
shielding them from the wind,
trying not to let them get crushed
under the weight of your hand
as you carry them forwards with you
into the big wide world.

GET THERE

I feel like I'm walking in circles,
staring out at the horizon,
wondering,
when will I have the faith
to follow the sun.

❀

I SEE YOU

For the ones
who are afraid
but have the courage
to keep going anyway.

❀

LET GO

You don't need to keep
holding on to the things
that are weighing you down.

Blooming

FEEL THINGS DEEPLY

I stumbled across a word the other day, and it hit me how I've never once thought of it as something to feel and aspire to... carefree – when was the last time I was carefree? When was the last time I didn't feel things so profoundly or go inward but let everything float above me? To just feel *light*.

Being someone who feels a lot, it's hard to know if being carefree is something I can and will feel. Maybe as the years go by and the memories fade. Maybe as the joy stretches further into my horizons and the worry sinks into the earth. Maybe then I'll feel carefree. It's also not that I don't have enough to lift me up: I just have too much weighing me down. Too many emotions, too many fears, too many worries.

I think to let go of it all and simply be 'carefree' for a day is not something you can choose to do. I don't think you can say, 'Today I'm going to be carefree,' and that's that. To be carefree, you have to shed the layers of the things weighing you down. You have to uncover the heaviness you've kept buried over the years and lay it to rest. Until eventually, the weight you hold becomes lighter: *you* become lighter.

So maybe then I'll feel carefree. Maybe then I'll have moments where I feel wild and unencumbered, my body shaking with ease. But I also think it's okay not to feel carefree right now. I'm not any less of a person because I take things into a deeper level inside of me, and therefore, take longer to find them and put them down again.

I have so many things, and maybe one day I'll be carefree too. But today, I'll honour the fact it's okay to be someone who feels things more deeply: the world needs people like us here too.

Blooming

When the sun rises and you rise with it,
too early for life and yet abundant
with morning bird song,
I hope you stay and lay awhile,
listening to it.
I hope you go forwards with
a grace and ease, knowing
you do not have to rush this day.
You are free to take your time.
You are free to move slowly
with a gentleness
as you begin to adjust to the day.

SIGNS YOU'RE DOING BETTER THAN YOU THINK…

You've stopped repressing emotions.
You're honouring your boundaries.
You're taking each day as it comes.
You're being gentle with yourself.
You're trusting in the unknown.
You're putting your needs first.
You're recognising your limits.
You're trying your best.
You're still here.

Everything is Always Changing

YOU COME FIRST

Why have you convinced yourself
your life's purpose is to
reply to messages, emails.
To keep saying yes:
to keep giving out.
You were not put on this earth
to say yes to everything and everyone –
suffocating your spirit into dust
until there's nothing left –
whilst forgetting to say yes to yourself.
You come first.
Your needs, your boundaries,
your energy – this comes first.
Stop accepting the idea
that you will *be* more
when you can *do* more for others,
and start embracing
your own requirements
before anything else.
You are too full
to have ever
been put on this earth
to continually drain yourself
for something or someone else.
Come back to you.

Blooming

Come back and centre on yourself:
you can give more out
only when you start giving
more in to yourself.
Your yes belongs to *you* first.

(Say no to others
before you say yes to yourself:
no is a really, really good word)

Everything is Always Changing

This loneliness you feel
weighing heavily on your heart
is because it feels like
you've gone back in time
to when you were eighteen.
When you had to watch
all your friends move on
with their lives.
And now,
here at twenty-four,
all your friends are
leaving you again:
promotions, masters,
moving in with partners,
spreading out so far and wide,
away from the only place
you've ever called home.
You're being left behind again,
and you feel so lonely.

But this time is *not*
the same as before.
It is not a repeat of history
because you are not heading
into a downhill health plunder.

Blooming

This time,
you are heading
into an uphill health lift.
You are coming out
on the other side of it:
you are expanding
into someone so new
and beautiful.
Yes,
they are still moving on
with their lives
without you,
but so are you.
You may be going slower,
your path so alien to theirs,
but you are growing
in your own beautiful way.
You *are* moving on too.

This is not like before.

ALONE NOT LONELY

There is comfort
in knowing that
even though you are alone,
with no one around you
to share these experiences with,
you are not lonely
within yourself
or to this earth
surrounding you...
There is a connection
in your arms;
falling into your own
internal universe.
There is a connection
in the stillness;
the pull of nature's magic,
the power the earth has
to make you feel *alive*.
So while you may have no one
to share this journey with,
you already have a connection
to yourself and this earth.
There is comfort in that...

Alone, not lonely.

Blooming

THE 3 PILLARS OF CONNECTION:

the connection to others
the connection to yourself
the connection to the earth

CONNECTION TO THE EARTH

Seek out the stillness
and the breathtaking quiet:
there is more life here
than anywhere else.

CONNECTION TO YOURSELF

The answers you seek are
lying dormant within you.
Pursue the calm you need
to hear them, and you
will discover all the truth
you've been searching for
is already inside you.

Everything is Always Changing

I was scared that letting go of my illness identity meant I would have nothing to write about – that I would lose this ability I love so much. But then I realised: I don't write about my illness. I write about how I feel. I write about my journey and healing. I write about the things I have learnt and the things I am still learning. My writing is not temporarily stuck with this illness; it is a part of me and who I am, and it will come with me wherever I go.

Letting go of how I've shaped and wrapped myself around my illness these past few years feels like starting over. It feels like letting go of a part of who I am and finding new pieces of myself to discover. And I will write my way through all of this. I will use my power of writing to move away from illness and into who I truly am. I will allow it to guide me and show me that everything I have gained in these past few years I will not lose if I let go of my illness.

Because sickness is not intertwined with everything else. I know this as I have seen people recover and find a new life away from what they once knew. But in this new life, they brought with them all the things they learnt from their time with illness. They carried the lessons, gratitude, healing techniques, love, and passions they discovered. The only thing they left behind was their illness and who they were as a sick person. And this is the only thing I'm going to leave behind too.

So I can let go of my illness identity knowing it is okay. I won't lose my writing, or the lessons, or anything else I want to keep. There is a whole life ahead of me with all the good things I have learnt to be carried forward with me.

※

Your illness may have caused
all these incredible things
to come into your life,
but if you take away your illness,
you won't take away
all the good things too:
they stay with you
wherever you go.

Everything is Always Changing

I crave freedom. And I'm not even sure freedom from what. I think because I've been tied down for so long, the idea of wide-open spaces and starlight skies leaves an aching on my heart. Maybe because, despite being free in my mind, I've spent so many years giving my body to something else. Something that keeps me tied down and dictates what I can and cannot do, where I can and cannot go.

Although, having lost both freedom of mind and body, I know that I would still choose to have freedom of mind. To know I can run into the worlds inside of me holds me through every waking moment. The knowledge that there is a safe place within that I can retreat to is the most valuable thing. And to understand I can find love and connection inside the depths of my soul is a discovery I'll always treasure.

But while freedom of mind is blissful, soul-enriching and beautiful, there's also a cliff edge: a boundary, a fall which you can see. You know you can only travel so far within the mind. You try to pretend it's real, that the freedom you have is all-encompassing. But you can see the ground beneath your feet isn't real, and reality looms in the distance.

But the thought of freedom of both mind and body, now that's something. It's something I crave and fold for. To be free: to wander through forests and dirt tracks and for your mind to be free with you. It's the ultimate kind of freedom. One I've tasted but never consumed. I'm so ready to step into this freedom now.

I can't help but wonder, is it selfish to want this: to want freedom of both mind and body? By the time I gained freedom of mind in my twenties, it was too late: the freedom of my body had gone. But because the new freedom in my head was so achingly beautiful – everything so still and quiet, tender and raw – I didn't ask for more as what I'd just gained was breathtaking.

But now I want more: I want both. And I know not everyone has the privilege to have freedom of body or mind. I know I'm one of the lucky ones to have this dream. So when it comes true – when this ache turns into reality, and my feet fall upon the ground. When I can travel down dirt roads and around mountain bends – I will go with the grace of someone who knows what it's like to have freedom of body and mind taken from them. I will go knowing the pain and mess and brokenness it took to regain this freedom back. I will go knowing few people in life have both, and often not through effort but luck. And I will go with the promise

that I will take this freedom and bury it in my bones
until I devour every ounce of it. I will hold it high and
make every use of it for all those who can't.

❋

It's okay to want more:
to think I deserve
more than this.
You have worked so hard
to get this far,
but you didn't work this hard
to *only* get this far.
You are allowed to keep dreaming:
you are allowed to keep aching
and stretching and hoping
that this effort will carry you
further than this.
And it will – you will keep going.
Maybe not always in the way you expected,
maybe not always in the way you hoped,
but you will still get *more*.
So keep dreaming and never settle:
more *is* coming for you.

Blooming

STILL SICK

I'm starting to understand
the sticky spot
of being so far from
where you once were,
all the focus
gets lost on this distance,
that people forget
you're still not anywhere near
where you should be.

❋

EASY IS BEAUTIFUL TOO

I think I've become
so attuned to
creating a beautiful life
alongside a hard one
that I forget
you don't need pain
to create a meaningful life:
life can be easy
and beautiful too.
Not everything worthwhile
has to be so hard.

Everything is Always Changing

WITHIN

It's okay if you're still not in the place you want to be.
It's okay to look around and feel...
disappointed that you haven't made it.
That you're still stuck and dreaming of being
somewhere else, anywhere but here.

But know this:
Outside, things may not have changed – no.
But inside – yes, this is where the change is happening.
This is where the magic is alive.

It doesn't mean
you still can't falter
when you see the mundanity
of your day to day routine.
But please don't ever forget
there is a life within you;
it's bending and folding and breaking you every day
just so you can keep evolving
and changing and growing.
No standstill on the outside
can ever cease the unrelenting
growth happening within you.

Look at you grow.

Blooming

I have two dates embedded in my mind that symbolise moments when my life changed. The first is 12th February 2013 – the day I contracted glandular fever, aged sixteen, which caused the onset of my chronic illness. The second is 29th November 2016 – the last day I left the house for nearly four years. Both dates mark the start of a different and irreversible life.

The 2013 date was the beginning of a journey I was not prepared for. The first three and a half years of my chronic illness were filled with so much unhappiness, anger and hurt. Whereas the 2016 date was the start of my inward healing journey. Even though my health continued to slip further each day, I started to embrace, accept, and surrender. I learnt how to be happy and peaceful despite everything.

But if I were to say which date holds more meaning to me, it would be 2013. Even though it was a dark and messy few years, I know how much I needed those years to go under. It was a process that I had to go through to reach the other side.

I don't believe everyone has to go through such darkness to find light, though. I think there are plenty of easier paths and other ways through. But as I already wasn't in a good place, it meant a lot of things had to happen to me first before my healing could begin.

So by declaring that my life changed in 2016 when my healing journey began feels incomplete. It doesn't feel right to forget the first few years just because they were hard. Because I was angry and hurting and didn't handle things 'right.' I think how I reacted was normal, considering what was going on.

By bringing the start point of my life-changing journey all the way back to sixteen-year-old me just feels like a big hug to her. An acceptance of the pain she had to go through. An acknowledgement that not coping well is nothing to be ashamed of. That healing is often feeling worse before you feel better.

So here's to embracing the light with the dark. Here's to acknowledging all the pain sixteen to nineteen-year-old me went through. And here's to owning our story, even the parts we're sorry our old self ever had to go through – knowing that at least they brought us home to the person we're proud to be today.

Blooming

YOU DECIDE

And that is the thing
with going through something
you never wanted to go through;
you cannot return
to who you were before.
You cannot pretend
everything is the same.
You have changed,
and nothing you do
can make you un-see
the things you have seen,
or take back the hardships
you have gone through.
But once you know this,
you realise
you have a choice:
you can stay here,
pretending you're the same,
ignoring the earthquake
that happened inside of you.
Or you can accept the change
and evolve into someone
you want to be.
If you do not like
who you have been made to become,

Everything is Always Changing

you do not have to stay like this.
While you may not be able to go back
into who you were before,
you can still go forward.
You can change,
again and again,
until you find
a version of yourself
you're happy with.
You do not have to let
what happened to you
define who you are.
You can choose
your own identity.
You have the power
to evolve
into someone else;
you have the ability
to change.
Don't let yourself
be defined by something
you don't want to be.
You decide who
you get to be.

Blooming

BE PROUD

I hope you're proud of all the times you rested even though you didn't want to.

I hope you're proud of all the times you said no.

I hope you're proud of all the times you did what was right for you.

I hope you're proud of all the times you stopped instead of pushing through.

I hope you're proud of all the times you put yourself first.

I hope you're proud of all the times you recognised your limits.

I hope you're proud of all the times you honoured your limits.

I hope you're proud of all the times you went at your own pace.

I hope you're proud of all the times you realised your best is, and always will be, enough.

RECOVERY

What does recovery look like to you? To me, it doesn't look like going back to my old, 'healthy' life. It's not staying out until 3am after a heavy evening of drinking. It's not pushing my body repeatedly to its limits until I become ill. It's not eating rubbish foods that don't fuel my mind or body. It's not being in a permanent state of stress, working until midnight. It's not being constantly busy, always on the go. It's not doing things I don't enjoy, being with people who make me feel small, or listening to those thoughts of criticism.

In fact, my idea of full recovery is not about going backwards to my pre-illness life at all. It's about doing the complete opposite of that. It's discovering a new meaning of the words 'healing' and 'recovery.' It's realising these words don't mean you then have permission to mistreat and neglect your body and mind but the opportunity to look after them.

To me, full recovery means being able to go for a walk because my body can. It means eating healthy, whole foods because it fuels me both mentally and physically. It's getting a good night sleep because that is the highest form of self-care. It's doing the things that I love because I should never waste my energy on things that bring me down rather than up. It's getting out of my comfort zone and pushing my body in terms of growth and learning. It's going fast *and* going slow; appreciating both speeds.

Recovery is not about going back to the place that got me ill in the first place at all; it's going forwards into the unknown. Into a place of self-care, gentleness, and compassion, but also joy, excitement, and gratitude. It's not about being 'boring' but being realistic. Recognising the so-called 'normal' life of not looking after yourself is not one to aspire to but to steer away from.

So while I'm now in 'recovery,' I'm aware I'm heading towards a completely unknown destination. I'm not going backwards. I'm heading into the wilderness where...
healing
courage
gratitude
happiness
messiness
and wholeness live.

I'm completely terrified, but also so excited to see where this journey will lead me.

BLOOM SILENTLY

Maybe, this is not
my time to shine.
Maybe, this is my time
to bloom silently by myself.

Maybe, I was meant to
start on the ground
and turn upwards.
Maybe, this is when
I'm supposed to bury my feet
into the earth,
throw my head back,
and appreciate
the horizons and stars
that have only become
visible to me in the past year
as I emerge from deep underground.

Maybe this is my time
to live for *me* after so long
being buried.
Maybe I bloom:
but silently and quietly,
as I figure out who I am
and work out where I belong

Blooming

amongst the stars.

Maybe, I was never meant to
bloom straight into the sun.
Maybe, this was always the time
to just appreciate
being here,
in the open,
as I gather my strength
to find out what it means
to be a part of this world again.

Maybe, I deserve that:
to let go
of needing to shine,
to succeed,
to be a light to others,
and instead,
become the light
I *need* for myself.

Everything is Always Changing

THE JOY IS TOO MUCH FOR WORDS

I'm aware of my absence of words about joy. You might think that maybe there has been little joy to talk about, but it's the opposite. There has been so much joy, and that's the problem. The thing is, every time I try to describe it – the moment, the feeling – nothing does it justice. No words, analogy or simile carry the weight of the pure joy and relief of improving.

The joy is drenching and overpowering and all-encompassing. I've cried so many times because the moment has been too much. Too many times, I've dreamt of this moment, and now it's happening, I can't process it. The tears speak the words I simply can't.

Maybe one day, I'll be able to put these feelings onto paper. Maybe one day I'll be the poet to my joy and write about these moments. But right now, I can only tell you about them. Stumbling over my words, and talk about the tears, the relief – the pure god damn relief – that my unshakable hope I grasped onto with everything I had for years wasn't a false dream: it was so, so real.

Let's stay in touch!

Follow me on social media:

Instagram: @mindfullyevie
(https://www.instagram.com/mindfullyevie/)
Facebook: @mindfullyevie
(https://www.facebook.com/mindfullyevie/)
Pinterest: Mindfully Evie
(https://www.pinterest.co.uk/mindfullyevie/)
Goodreads: Mindfully Evie
(https://www.goodreads.com/mindfullyevie)

My blog: www.mindfullyevie.com

For all enquires: evie@mindfullyevie.com

Please note that 10% of all profits from the book
sales will go to charity, split equally between 'Invest in
M.E' and 'Lyme Disease Action'. To find out more
about these charities, visit:
http://www.investinme.org/
https://www.lymediseaseaction.org.uk

xx

Printed in Great Britain
by Amazon